P9-DXT-191

CLASSICS *for* YOUNG READERS

TABLE OF CONTENTS

LESSONS LEARNED

MOSTLY HEROES

FAVORITES FROM FAMOUS BOOKS

STORIES FROM THE BIBLE

POETRY

SEASONAL CHANGE

PASSING MOMENTS

LESSONS LEARNED

Salt and Bread

There was once a king with three daughters. The two older girls were jealous of the youngest, whom the King loved very dearly, and they spent much time and effort trying to destroy the King's love for her. They tried to win special favors and privileges from their father, never missing an opportunity to suggest that the youngest girl did not return his affection. Their evil jealousy would not let them rest.

At last the old king became troubled over the rumors he heard from the older daughters. He even became suspicious of the youngest girl. And one day when the three girls were with him, he could not refrain from putting their love to a test.

So he asked the oldest girl to tell him how much she loved him, and she replied:

"I value you, my father, as God in Heaven!"

Her answer pleased the King. He then asked the second daughter the same question, and she replied:

"Oh my father, I value you as my own life!"

This answer also pleased the King. And he turned now to the youngest daughter, asking her how she could describe her feelings. She answered:

"Oh my father, I value you as salt and bread."

The King was startled by this reply. Then he became angry that she cared no more for him than the humblest things on a poor man's table. His anger turned to fury that his youngest daughter, on whom he had lavished so much affection, thought so little of him in return. And he ordered his servants to drive her out of his house. They did as they were told, and took her into the woods and abandoned her. Now, at last, the two older daughters were happy.

In the woods, the youngest daughter was miserable and frightened. She cried when she thought about home and the father she loved. She could not understand his anger, nor why she had been banished. She wandered about the woods hopelessly, and at last, in fear of the wild animals, climbed into a tall tree.

It happened that a king from another country at this moment was hunting in the woods. As he rode along on his horse, he heard his dogs barking in excitement. He hurried after them and found them surrounding the tree where the Princess was hiding. He looked upward, expecting to find a bear. Instead, he saw the beautiful face of the unhappy girl. He spoke to her kindly and asked her to come down.

He put the girl on his horse and took her to his castle. There he fed her and warmed her before a log fire. At last, overcome by his kindness, the Princess poured out her story. The King was impressed with her goodness as well as her beauty. He cared for her in his castle, and at last he asked her to marry him. The girl, too, had fallen in love, and she agreed.

So a date was set for the wedding, and invitations were sent to the royalty of the seven neighboring kingdoms. When the wedding day came, the royal guests arrived. Among them were the young Princess's father and two older sisters. They did not recognize her, so sure they were that the young Princess had disappeared forever into the woods.

When they took their seats at the banquet table, wonderful food of all kinds was set before the guests. But none of the food was salted, and there was no salt on the table. Neither was there bread.

At last the girl's father could not refrain from commenting, and he said, "I don't understand, but it seems that the two most precious things are missing from this feast."

"Ah?" the Princess, now a Queen, replied. "What can you be speaking of?"

"Why," her father replied, "salt and bread."

"Yes," the girl said. "They are among the most precious things we know. And once because I valued my father as highly as these things I was driven out of his house to the woods to die."

When her father heard the words, he was overcome. He recognized her and embraced her with a cry of joy, thankful and happy that she was alive and well. He begged her forgiveness for his misunderstanding of her words of affection, and for having her driven away.

As for the older sisters, their plot against the youngest was now exposed, and it was their turn to be turned out of their father's house. From that day on, no more was ever heard of them. If they were ever rescued from the woods by hunting kings, nobody has ever heard about it.

ALI AND THE MAGIC STEW
by Shulamith Levey Oppenheim

Long ago in Persia there lived a boy named Ali ibn Ali. His father was a wealthy merchant. His mother was a woman of beauty and kindness. His home was a palace where fountains overflowed into deep reflecting pools. As he had no brothers or sisters, he was the apricot of his parents' eyes.

Fortunate as Ali ibn Ali was in worldly gifts, he was also most unfortunate, for he had grown spoiled and selfish.

"Disgusting grapes!" A handful of fruit flew through the air. Ali was sitting cross-legged with Layla, his small black monkey, on his shoulder. "They are fit only for the beggar who fouls our gate!"

At that moment Ali's parents entered. If Ali had one spot in his heart that raced with love, it was for his parents.

"What are we hearing?" His father peered at his son. "That is no way to speak, beloved child." His mother kissed him.

"These grapes are rotten, Father." Ali threw his arms around his father's neck. "They are fit only for the bowl of that beggar who crowds our gate. Why do you allow him to sit here?" Ali stroked his father's cheek.

His mother took Ali's slim, ringed fingers in hers. "A true Muslim gives to the poor, the crippled, the homeless, the hungry. This man is all of these."

"And," his father put palms together before his face, "as he chooses to bless our gate, there he shall remain. Now, I have something to tell you."

Ali jumped up, his face flushed. "Father, are you going away? Mother, tell him he mustn't go away again so soon. We're lonely when he's gone. So is Layla." His mother said nothing, but Ali knew she, too, wished her husband to stay.

"Only a few days, my son. Take care of your mother. And no more ugly tempers. Such behavior is unacceptable at any age!"

That evening Ali and his mother watched as the merchant galloped off on his favorite horse, followed by three servants, their saddlebags bulging with spices and gems. But in two days he was brought back on a litter, racked with fever and pain in all his limbs.

During the next hours doctors and wise men examined the suffering merchant. Each emerged bewildered, leaving mixes of herbs and potions.

Ali held Layla close. Whenever his eyes overflowed with tears, the monkey wiped the boy's cheeks with her small paws.

"What shall we do, Layla? Mother sits by Father's bed day and night cooling his face with rose water. We must help."

Ali tiptoed to the door of his father's room and knocked softly. "Come," his mother answered. His father lay in a high, canopied bed. His skin was the color of ivory. Ali had never seen his mother's face so sad, so pale.

"The fever is raging," she whispered. "He does not eat or drink. And his words ..." She stifled a sob. "He mutters, but ..."

Ali leaned close to his father's mouth. "Father, do you wish to tell us something?" The invalid made a move to lift his hand, but it fell limply onto the coverlet.

"Shhhh ... llla." It was barely audible. "MMMMMba, kah ... kah ... la ... ba ..."

Ali turned to his mother. His eyes were bright. "I think, Mother, that father is trying to say *shula kalambar*. Would he ask for this? It's a tasty stew, but ..."

"Shula kalambar. It isn't a favorite of his. It *is* tasty, but there are many delicacies he enjoys far more. Honey cakes and rice creams and grilled lamb with allspice."

Ali knelt beside the bed. "Am I right, Father? Shula kalambar?" There was a slight but distinct move of his father's head.

Ali raced from the room, across the courtyard to the kitchens.

"Cook, we must have shula kalambar," he commanded in his imperious tone. "My father requests it!"

"Regrets, young master!" The cook bowed. "We have lentils and garlic but not spinach and coriander. These must be of the freshest."

Ali stamped his foot. "Get them!"

The cook answered. "My kitchen boys are not here, and I cannot leave. There is baklava in the oven for your honored mother. I—"

"I don't care about *you*!" Ali shook with rage. "Very well, I shall get them myself!"

He ran to his chamber, where he took gold coins from a bronze box and tucked them into the pocket of his silk tunic. Then he raced to the outer gate. As he passed through, he tripped over the beggar's bowl. "Pig!" Ali could feel the blood oozing from his knee. With a sharp intake of breath, he pulled up against the gate, brushing the beggar's shoulder.

"Steady, Ali ibn Ali." The beggar's voice was musical. "There is time before the stalls close."

The words stunned Ali. "How do you know I am going to the market stalls?"

The man shifted position. "I know. I also know that you are correct; your father did ask for shula kalambar. The stew has

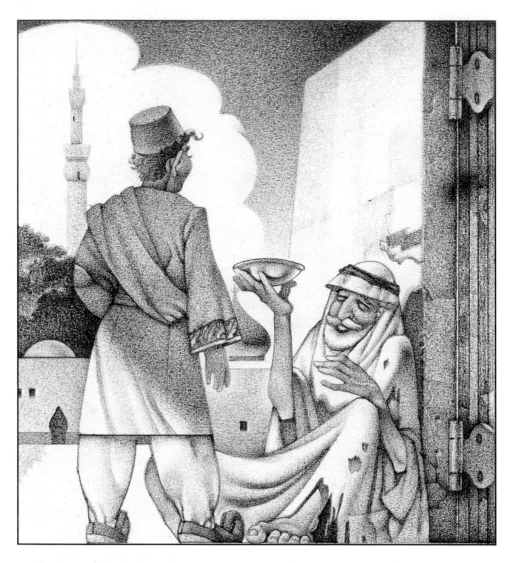

great healing powers, but," he raised a knobbed finger, "for it to work, *all* ingredients must be purchased with coins begged from the street. Garlic, coriander, spinach, lentils ... all."

"Begged from the street!" Fear and fury shot through the boy's slight frame. "Then give me what you have. I will give you gold coins in exchange."

"Ah, Ali ibn Ali, it is not that simple. The coins must be obtained by a family member for the healing to work."

A family member! He looked down at the beggar. "Why should I believe you? You sit here in the dust by my father's grace. What do you know of the world?"

The beggar looked up, his heavy-lidded eyes half closed. "There is no reason to believe me, young master. But if you wish to save your father, heed my words."

Layla was racing around and around Ali's feet, chattering and pulling his trousers. Ali's head whirled. Strangely, every bone in his body was suddenly pushing him to do as the beggar instructed. However much be abhorred this creature, he must carry out the necessary actions so that his father would again be well and roses would again bloom in his mother's cheeks.

"Then I shall beg," he replied. Ali threw back his shoulders and straightened his turban with its diamond plume. "No one will deny me. I have only to ask."

As he turned to leave, the beggar caught him by the belt of his tunic. The boy recoiled, but the beggar held fast. "Begged from the street, in the clothes of a beggar, hunched as a beggar, with a beggar's bowl." The beggar closed his eyes.

Fine blue veins rose up under the skin of Ali's temples. Quickly he removed his turban and tunic. As he did so, the beggar threw off his ragged cloak with an agility that belied his wizened appearance and handed it to the boy. Ali laid the tunic and turban next to the beggar. Then he smeared his face with dust, threw the cloak over his head, put Layla on his shoulder, took up the bowl, and set out.

Bent over, Ali held out the bowl, his eyes averted from the scornful gaze of passersby. "Please, sir," Ali ran toward a richly dressed man and woman, "please, lady, for my father who is dying. For a stew to heal him. Please, for the love of Allah."

The couple sneered, but the woman opened her gold-mesh purse and dropped a coin into the bowl. As Ali leaned forward, the man shoved him aside with a force that sent the boy and monkey across the cobbles. The coin flew from the bowl.

"A dying father! There's a new one! What lies these pigs invent to take our gold."

Ali crawled after the coin, heedless of the jeers. "Out of sight, son of filth," the man called after him.

It was Layla who retrieved the coin. Ali stood up. The tears that had been brimming in his eyes ran down his cheeks, leaving streaks through the grime and dirt. He felt a soft paw touch each eye. "It's all right, Layla. We *must* beg enough to buy lentils and garlic and spinach and coriander. We must. But how can people be so cruel? I've feelings, too, under these rags."

So Ali ibn Ali started out again, repeating his pleas until the sun was low behind the mountains and his limbs could barely crouch. Jeers of "Fool" and "Filth" and "Useless flesh," scenes of shame were repeated again and again. Finally, as darkness fell, there was a handful of coins in the bowl. Ali raced to the market. He found one tiny stall open. His hands trembled as he paid. Layla clung to his arm, her tail wound loosely around his neck. With the precious items in a sleeve of the cloak, he raced back to the palace.

The beggar was sitting as Ali had left him, his head on his chest. Tunic and turban lay beside him. Ali stopped to catch his breath. "I pray Allah you are right, old man," he whispered. "How unkind people were, all because they thought I was poor, that I was begging, because ..." He stopped. Something tugged at his chest.

The beggar opened one eye. "And because you have begged and have the ingredients for the stew, you had better have the shula kalambar prepared immediately, Ali ibn Ali."

Ali shot to the kitchen where the chief cook was about to toss him out until he revealed himself. Ali requested politely, to his own astonishment as well as to everyone else's, that the stew be prepared instantly.

With Layla on his back, Ali carried the steaming dish past the fountains to his parents' room.

He put a finger to his lips in reply to his mother's amazement at the sight of him in rags, his face a smudge of dust and grime. "I'll tell you later, beloved Mother. Now Father must eat."

Ali's mother put a hand under her husband's head. "Eat, beloved, eat," she urged as Ali put a spoonful of stew to his father's lips.

"Eat, Father. For Mother, for me, for Layla, for yourself above all." To himself he added, "Please, Allah, let this stew heal my father. Let the beggar be right. I will give him anything he desires. I have learned so much in these last hours. I—"

"Ali!" His mother gave a cry. "Look at his face! Is there not a rosy hue blushing his cheeks?"

It was true! The invalid was breathing more lightly. His eyelids fluttered, then a smile began to play about his lips. A moment later his eyes opened. Ali could barely hold steady the next spoonful.

"Give me the bowl." His mother took the stew from Ali. "I will feed him now. You must wash from head to toe and throw away that rag you are wearing. Where in Allah's name ..."

"No, my son!" It was his father, in a clear, strong voice. "Do not throw away the cloak. Let it ever be a reminder that the gentle heart brings life and joy."

"I will never forget, Father." Ali kissed his father's hand and, leaving the room, ran back to the gate of the palace and fell on his knees before the beggar. "May I keep your cloak? My father will provide you with a new one. Two. As many as you wish."

The beggar took up a stick that lay beside him and, with great effort, started to pull himself up.

"Keep the cloak, Ali ibn Ali. Keep it as a reminder of the pain unkindness brings. And don't forget to take your own clothes back. And tell your honorable father I accept his gifts."

Ali put his arms around the man's shoulders to steady him. "Where are you going? I want you to stay."

"I am going and I am staying," the beggar said, nodding gravely. Then his face burst into a mass of smiling creases. "I am staying and I am going. Your father will grow strong again. Roses will bloom in your mother's cheeks. And you," the beggar touched Ali's forehead, "will be a source of pride and joy to your parents now and in their old age." And the beggar melted into the darkness.

THE FIRE ON THE MOUNTAIN

an Ethiopian folktale
retold by Harold Courlander and Wolf Leslau

People say that in the old days in the city of Addis Ababa there was a young man by the name of Arha. He had come as a boy from the country of Guragé, and in the city he became the servant of a rich merchant, Haptom Hasei.

Haptom Hasei was so rich that he owned everything that money could buy, and often he was very bored because he had tired of everything he knew, and there was nothing new for him to do.

One cold night, when the damp wind was blowing across the plateau, Haptom called to Arha to bring wood for the fire. When Arha was finished, Haptom began to talk.

"How much cold can a man stand?" he said, speaking at first to himself. "I wonder if it would be possible for a man to stand on the highest peak, Mount Sululta, where the coldest winds blow, through an entire night, without blankets or clothing, and yet not die?"

"I don't know," Arha said. "But wouldn't it be a foolish thing?"

"Perhaps, if he had nothing to gain by it, it would be a foolish thing to spend the night that way," Haptom said. "But I would be willing to bet that a man couldn't do it."

"I am sure a courageous man could stand naked on Mount Sululta throughout an entire night and not die of it," Arha said. "But as for me, it isn't my affair since I've nothing to bet."

"Well, I'll tell you what," Haptom said. "Since you are so sure it can be done, I'll make a bet with you anyway. If you can stand among the rocks on Mount Sululta for an entire night, without food or water or clothing or blankets or fire, and not die of it, then I will give you ten acres of good farmland for your own, with a house and cattle."

Arha could hardly believe what he had heard.

"Do you really mean this?" he asked.

"I am a man of my word," Haptom replied.

"Then tomorrow night I will do it," Arha said, "and afterwards, for all the years to come, I shall till my own soil."

But he was very worried, because the wind swept bitterly across the peak. So in the morning Arha went to a wise old man from the Guragé tribe and told him of the bet he had made. The old man listened quietly and thoughtfully, and when Arha had finished he said:

"I will help you. Across the valley from Sululta is a high rock, which can be seen in the daytime. Tomorrow night, as the sun goes down, I shall build a fire there, so that it can be seen from where you stand on the peak. All night long you must watch the light of my fire. Do not close your eyes or let the darkness creep upon you. As you watch my fire, think of its warmth, and think of me, your friend, sitting there tending it for you. If you do this, you will survive, no matter how bitter the night wind."

Arha thanked the old man warmly and went back to Haptom's house with a light heart. He told Haptom he was ready, and in the afternoon Haptom sent him, under the watchful eyes of other servants, to the top of Mount Sululta. There, as night fell, Arha removed his clothes and stood in the damp cold wind that swept across the plateau with the setting sun. Across the valley, several miles away, Arha saw the light of his friend's fire, which shone like a star in the blackness.

The wind turned colder and seemed to pass through his flesh and chill the marrow in his bones. The rock on which he stood felt like ice. Each hour the cold numbed him more, until he thought he would never be warm again, but he kept

his eyes upon the twinkling light across the valley and remembered that his old friend sat there tending a fire for him. Sometimes wisps of fog passed. He sneezed and coughed and shivered and began to feel ill. Yet all night through he stood there, and only when the dawn came did he put on his clothes and go down the mountain back to Addis Ababa.

Haptom was very surprised to see Arha, and he questioned his servants thoroughly.

"Did he stay all night without food or drink or blankets or clothing?"

"Yes," his servants said. "He did all of these things."

"Well, you are a strong fellow," Haptom said to Arha. "How did you manage to do it?"

"I simply watched the light of a fire on a distant hill," Arha said.

"What! You watched a fire! Then you lose the bet, and you are still my servant, and you own no land!"

"But this fire was not close enough to warm me; it was far across the valley!"

"I won't give you the land," Haptom said. "You didn't fulfill the conditions. It was only the fire that saved you."

Arha was very sad. He went again to his friend of the Guragé tribe and told him what had happened.

"Take the matter to the judge," the old man advised him.

Arha went to the judge and complained, and the judge sent for Haptom. When Haptom told his story, and the servants said once more that Arha had watched a distant fire across the valley, the judge said: "No, you have lost, for Haptom Hasei's condition was that you must be without fire."

Once more Arha went to his old friend with the sad news that he was doomed to the life of a servant, as though he had not gone through the ordeal on the mountaintop.

"Don't give up hope," the old man said. "More wisdom grows wild in the hills than in any city judge."

He got up from where he sat and went to find a man named Hailu, in whose house he had been a servant when he was young. He explained to the good man about the bet between Haptom and Arha, and asked if something couldn't be done.

"Don't worry about it," Hailu said after thinking for a while. "I will take care of it for you."

Some days later Hailu sent invitations to many people in the city to come to a feast at his house. Haptom was among them, and so was the judge who had ruled Arha had lost the bet.

When the day of the feast arrived, the guests came riding on mules with fine trappings, their servants strung out behind them on foot. Haptom came with twenty servants, one of whom held a silk umbrella over his head to shade him from the sun, and four drummers played music that signified the great Haptom was there.

The guests sat on soft rugs laid out for them and talked. From the kitchen came the odors of wonderful things to eat: roast goat, roast corn and durra, pancakes called injera, and many tantalizing sauces. The smell of the food only accentuated the hunger of the guests. Time passed. The food should have been served, but they didn't see it, only smelled vapors that drifted from the kitchen. The evening came and still no food was served. The guests began to whisper among themselves. It was very curious that the honorable Hailu had not had the food brought out. Still the smells came from the kitchen. At last one of the guests spoke out for all the others:

"Hailu, why do you do this to us? Why do you invite us to a feast and then serve us nothing?"

"Why, can't you smell the food?" Hailu asked with surprise.

"Indeed we can, but smelling is not eating; there is no nourishment in it."

"And is there warmth in a fire so distant that it can hardly be seen?" Hailu asked. "If Arha was warmed by the fire he watched while standing on Mount Sululta, then you have been fed by the smells coming from my kitchen."

The people agreed with him; the judge now saw his mistake, and Haptom was ashamed. He thanked Hailu for his advice, and announced that Arha was then and there the owner of the land, the house, and the cattle.

Then Hailu ordered the food brought in, and the feast began.

THE SWORD OF DAMOCLES

retold by James Baldwin

There was once a king whose name was Dionysius. He was so unjust and cruel that he won for himself the name of a tyrant. He knew that almost everybody hated him, and so he was always in dread lest someone should take his life.

But he was very rich, and he lived in a fine palace where there were many beautiful and costly things. And he was waited upon by a host of servants who were always ready to do his bidding.

One day a friend of his, whose name was Damocles, said to him, "How happy you must be! You have here everything that any man could wish."

"Perhaps you would like to change places with me," said the tyrant.

"No, not that, O king!" said Damocles. "But I think that if I could only have your riches and your pleasures for one day, I should not want any greater happiness."

"Very well," said the tyrant. "You shall have them."

And so, the next day, Damocles was led into the palace, and all the servants were bidden to treat him as their master. He sat down at a table in the banquet hall, and rich foods were placed before him. He lacked nothing that could give him pleasure. There were costly wines, and beautiful flowers, and rare perfumes, and delightful music. He rested among soft cushions, and felt that he was the happiest man in the world.

Then he chanced to raise his eyes toward the ceiling. What was it dangling above him, with its point almost touching his head? It was a sharp sword, and it was hung by only a single horsehair. What if the hair should break? There was danger every moment that it would do so.

The smile faded from the lips of Damocles. His face became ashy pale. His hands trembled. He wanted no more food; he could drink no more wine; he took no more delight in the music. He longed to be out of the palace, far away, he cared not where.

"What is the matter?" said the tyrant.

"That sword! That sword!" cried Damocles. He was so badly frightened that he dared not move.

"Yes," said Dionysius, "I know there is a sword above your head, and it may fall at any moment. But why should that trouble you? I have a sword over my head all the time. I am every moment in dread lest something may cause me to lose my life."

"Let me go," said Damocles. "I now see that I was mistaken, and that the rich and powerful are not so happy as they seem. Let me go back to my cottage among the mountains."

And so long as he lived, he never again wanted to change places with the king.

As Rich As Croesus

retold by James Baldwin

Some thousands of years ago there lived in Asia a king whose name was Croesus. The country over which he ruled was not very large, but its people were prosperous and famed for their wealth. Croesus himself was said to be the richest man in the world. So well known is his name that, to this day, people say of a very wealthy person that he is "as rich as Croesus."

King Croesus had everything that could make him happy—lands and houses, fine clothing to wear, and beautiful things to look at. He could not think of anything he needed to make him more comfortable or contented. "I am the happiest man in the world," he said.

It happened one summer that a great man from across the sea was traveling in Asia. The name of this man was Solon. He was the lawmaker of Athens in ancient Greece. He was noted for his wisdom. Even long after his death, people would praise a wise man by saying, "He is as wise as Solon."

Solon had heard of Croesus, and so one day he visited him in his beautiful palace. Croesus was now happier and prouder than ever before, for the wisest man in the world was his guest.

He led Solon through his palace. He showed him the grand rooms, the fine carpets, the soft couches, the rich furniture, the pictures, the books. Then he invited him out to see his gardens and his orchards and his stables. He showed him thousands of rare and beautiful things that he collected from all parts of the world.

In the evening, the wisest of men and the richest of men dined together. The king said to his guest, "Tell me, Solon, who do you think is the happiest of all men?" He expected that Solon would say, "Croesus."

The wise man was silent for a minute. And then he said, "I have in mind a man who once lived in Athens and whose name was Tellus. He, I doubt not, is the happiest of all men."

This was not the answer that Croesus wanted. But he hid his disappointment and asked, "Why do you think so?"

"Because," answered his guest, "Tellus was an honest man. He labored hard for many years to bring up his children and give them a good education. And when they were grown and able to take care of themselves, he joined the Athenian army and gave his life bravely in the defense of his country. Can you think of anyone who is more deserving of happiness?"

"Perhaps not," answered Croesus, half choking with disappointment. "But who do you think ranks next to Tellus in happiness?" He was quite sure now that Solon would say Croesus.

"I have in mind," said Solon, "two young men whom I knew in Greece. Their father died when they were mere children, and they were very poor. But they worked to keep the house together and to support their feeble mother. Year after year they toiled, with no thought of anything but their mother's comfort. When at last she died, they gave their love to Athens, their native city, and served nobly as long as they lived."

Then Croesus was angry. "Why is it," he asked, "that you think my wealth and power are nothing? Why is it that you place these poor working people above the richest king in the world?"

"O king," said Solon, "no man can say whether you are happy or not until you die. For no man knows what misfortunes may overtake you, or what misery may be yours in place of all this splendor."

Many years after this there arose in Asia a powerful king named Cyrus. At the head of a great army he marched from one country to another, overthrowing many a kingdom and attaching it to his great empire in Babylon. King Croesus with all his wealth was not able to stand against this mighty warrior. He resisted as long as he could. Then his city was taken and his beautiful palace burned. His orchards and gardens were destroyed, his treasures were carried away, and he himself was made prisoner.

"The stubbornness of this man Croesus," said King Cyrus, "has caused us much trouble and the loss of many good soldiers. Take him and make an example of him for others who may dare to stand in our way."

The soldiers seized Croesus and dragged him to the marketplace. Then they built up a great pile of dry sticks and timber taken from the ruins of his once beautiful palace. When this was finished, they tied the unhappy king in the midst of it, and one ran for a torch to set it on fire.

"Now we shall have a merry blaze," said the brutal fellows. "What good can all his wealth do him now?"

As poor Croesus, bruised and bleeding, lay without a friend to soothe his misery, he thought of the words Solon had spoken to him years before. "No man can say whether you are happy or not until you die," he moaned. "O Solon! Solon! Solon!"

It so happened that Cyrus was riding by at that very moment and heard his moans. "What does he say?" he asked of the soldiers.

"He says, 'Solon, Solon, Solon!'" answered one.

Then the king rode nearer and asked Croesus, "Why do you call on the name of Solon?"

Croesus was silent at first. But after Cyrus had repeated his question kindly, he told all about Solon's visit at his palace and what he had said.

The story affected Cyrus deeply. He thought of the words, "No man knows what misfortunes may overtake you, or what misery may be yours in place of all this splendor." And he wondered if sometime he, too, would lose all his power and be helpless in the hands of his enemies.

"After all," said he, "shouldn't we be merciful and kind to those in distress? I will do to Croesus as I would have others do to me." And he caused Croesus to be given his freedom, and ever afterward treated him as one of his most honored friends.

THE THREE QUESTIONS

by Leo Tolstoy

It once occurred to a certain king that he would never fail in anything if he always knew the answers to three questions: How can I know the right time for every action? Who are the people most important to me and to whom I ought to give the greatest attention? And above all, what is the most important thing to do?

The king proclaimed that he would bestow a large reward on anyone who could answer his three questions.

Learned men began coming to the king, but they all gave different answers.

In reply to the first question, some said that to know the right time for every action, the king must draw up a schedule of days, months, and years, and strictly stick to it. Only in this way, they said, could he do everything at the proper time.

Others said it was impossible for one man to decide the proper time for every action. They urged the king to have a council of wise men and act according to their advice.

Another group said that certain matters required immediate decision. For such matters, the king could not wait to ask wise men whether it was the right time to take action. "The only way you can know if it is the right time to act," they said, "is to know in advance what is going to happen. Only a magician can know this. Therefore, in order to know the right time for every action, you must consult the magicians."

The king also received many different answers to his second question: Who are the people most important to me and to whom I ought to give the greatest attention? Some said that the people most important to the king were his administrators. Some said the priests. Some said the physicians. Others said the warriors.

To his third question—What is the most important thing to do?—the king received equally diverse answers. Some said that science was the most important pursuit in the world. Some said military skill. Others said religious worship.

The answers were all different. Therefore, the king agreed with none of them, and rewarded no one.

In order to find the true answers to his questions, he decided to consult a hermit who was famous for his wisdom.

The hermit never left the forest where he lived, and there he would speak only with plain folk. So the king dressed himself as one of the people. Well before he reached the hermit's dwelling, he dismounted. He left his knights behind and went on alone.

The king found the hermit digging a garden in front of his hut. When he saw the king, the hermit greeted him and returned to his digging. He was thin and frail, and each time he thrust his spade into the ground and turned a little clod of earth, he breathed heavily.

The king said, "I have come to see you, wise hermit, to ask you for the answers to three questions: How can I know the right time for every action, so that I do not allow some important act to slip by only to regret it later? Who are the people most important to me and to whom I ought to give the greatest attention? And, what is the most important thing to do, which therefore I ought to do first?"

The hermit listened to the king, but gave him no answer. He merely spat on his hands and started digging again. "You have exhausted yourself," the king said. "Give me the spade. I'll work for a while."

"Thanks," said the hermit. He handed him the spade and sat down on the ground.

After digging two beds, the king stopped and repeated his questions. The hermit did not answer, but got up and held out his hand for the spade, saying, "Now you rest and I'll work."

But the king did not give him the spade. He went on digging.

An hour passed, then another. The sun had begun to sink behind the trees when the king stuck the spade into the ground and said, "I came to you, wise man, for answers to my questions. If you can give me none, tell me so and I shall return home."

"Here comes someone running," said the hermit. "Let us see who it is."

The king looked around and saw a bearded man running out of the woods. The man held his hands pressed to his stomach. His fingers were covered with blood. He ran up to the king and fell fainting to the ground, where he lay still, weakly moaning.

The king and the hermit opened the man's clothing. There was a large wound in his stomach. The king washed it as well as he could and bandaged it with his own handkerchief and the hermit's towel. When the blood at last ceased flowing, the wounded man revived and asked for water. The king brought fresh water and gave him a drink.

Meanwhile the sun had set and it grew cool. The king, with the hermit's help, carried the wounded man into the hut and laid him on the bed. He closed his eyes and grew still.

The king was so tired from the work he had done that he lay down and fell asleep. He slept soundly through the short summer night. When he woke, it was some time before he realized where he was and recalled the bearded stranger lying on the bed, who was now staring at him with shining eyes.

"Forgive me," said the bearded man in a faint voice, when he saw that the king was awake and looking at him.

"I do not know you and have nothing to forgive you," replied the king.

"You do not know me, but I know you. I am your enemy, and I swore to take vengeance on you for the death of my brother and the loss of my property. I knew you had come alone to see the hermit, and I resolved to kill you on your way back. But when the whole day passed and you did not return, I left to seek you out and came upon your knights instead. They recognized me, attacked me, and wounded me. I escaped from them, but I would have bled to death if you had not cared for my wound. I intended to kill you, and you have saved my life. Now, if I live, and if you wish it, I will serve you faithfully. Forgive me!"

The king was happy to be reconciled with his enemy. He not only forgave him but also promised to return his property and send his own physician and servants to attend him.

The king left the wounded man and went out to look for the hermit. He wished for the last time to ask him to answer his questions. The hermit was on his knees in the yard, sowing seeds in the beds that had been dug the day before.

The king approached him and said, "For the last time, wise man, I ask you to answer my questions."

"But you have already been answered," said the hermit, squatting on his thin calves and looking up at the king who stood before him.

"How have I been answered?" asked the king.

"How?" repeated the hermit. "Had you not taken pity on my weakness yesterday and dug these beds for me, instead of turning back alone, that fellow would have assaulted you, and you would have regretted not staying with me. Therefore, the most important time was when you were digging the beds. I was the most important man. And the most important pursuit was to do good to me.

"And later, when the man came running to us, the most important time was when you were taking care of him, for if you had not bound up his wound, he would have died without having made peace with you. Therefore, he was the most important man. And what you did for him was the most important deed.

"Remember then: there is only one important time—*Now*. It is important because it is the only time when we are masters of ourselves. And the most important man is *he with whom you are,* for no one can know whether or not he will ever have dealings with any other man. And the most important thing to do is *to do good to him,* since it is for that purpose alone that man was sent into this life."

MOSTLY HEROES

THE STORY OF MULAN

a Chinese legend
retold by Vanessa Wright

1. THE DRAGON ROARS

Mulan's nimble fingers danced over her weaving. Slowly, two glittering eyes began to gaze out from among the threads. Mulan's younger brother watched as the rest of the mighty dragon took form in the cloth. Suddenly, he cried, "ROAR! ROAR!" and ran away as fast as his chubby legs could carry him.

Laughing, Mulan jumped up from her stool and chased the boy around their family's home, through the courtyard, across the road, almost to the bank of the Yellow River.

"Got you!" cried Mulan, hugging her brother close. "I caught a dragon!"

"ROAR!" he shouted, struggling to free himself, "ROAR! ROAR! ROAR!"

At that moment, a guard of the emperor's soldiers clattered up the lane. Mulan and her brother fell silent. Soldiers like these had never before come to the quiet village. For a moment, Mulan let go of her brother. He darted out into the lane, almost underneath the horses' heavy hooves.

"ROAR! ROAR!" he cried.

The lead soldier reined in his horse. He picked the little boy up off the ground with one hand and snarled, "So, little dragon, are you coming with us to fight the enemy in the north?"

Mulan approached the soldiers. "I am sorry my brother got in your way," she said. "Please put him down."

"What's this? A nightingale, too? Beware your tongue, nightingale—my sword is sharp!" the lead soldier growled.

The other soldiers looked uncomfortable. Mulan's little brother began to whimper.

"Put my brother down," said Mulan.

The lead soldier narrowed his eyes and directed a cold, hard stare at Mulan. Mulan stared back. She did not flinch. The soldier's horse snorted and pawed the ground. After a long moment, the soldier dropped the boy. "You won't fight, boy," he sneered, "but your father will." He turned to his troop. "Ride!" he bellowed, and the soldiers cantered away.

Mulan's little brother stood up and wiped the dust off his face. "What did the man mean about Father?" he asked.

"I don't know," said Mulan, "but I'm going to find out."

Mulan took her brother home and then ran to the marketplace. The soldiers had posted twelve scrolls. People pressed and pushed to read the scrolls. Their sobs and cries filled the air.

"What is the matter?" Mulan asked an old woman. "What is going on?"

"There is a war in the north," replied the old woman. "The Emperor has ordered every grown man to go and fight. The names of the men who must go are written on the scrolls."

Mulan thanked the old woman and threaded her way through the crowd to read the names on the scrolls.

The first name she saw was her father's. Mulan swayed where she stood.

"Are you all right?" someone asked.

"My father's name is on the list," said Mulan. "But he cannot go to war. My father is too old to fight."

"He must go. If he does not, the Emperor will punish him and your whole family."

"Surely there is another way!"

"If your father wishes, he may send your older brother in his place. Then he will not have to fight."

"But I have no older brother," thought Mulan. She turned, pushed her way out of the crowd, and ran from the marketplace.

At the edge of the river, she cried until she had no more tears. She splashed some water on her face. But when the river smoothed and showed her reflection, Mulan saw a strong face, a brave face.

"A boy's face," Mulan breathed.

That night, Mulan knelt before her parents and told them of her plan. "I will dress as a young man and go to war in Father's place."

Her mother wept. Her father argued. But neither tears nor reproach swayed the young girl.

In the morning, she set out for the marketplace once more, this time to buy a saddle and a good, strong horse to ride to the war in the north.

When she came home, she changed from her silk robes into her father's leather and iron armor. She swept up her hair and fastened her helmet. As she turned to leave her room, she glimpsed her face in the mirror. She brushed her fingertips against the cold glass.

"Is that me?" she wondered.

Mulan led her horse into the courtyard. Her father helped her tie his sword, spear, and shield to her saddle. Mulan's mother handed her a satchel bulging with food.

"This should keep you until you arrive at Black Mountain," she said through her tears.

Mulan's little brother ran up carrying a stick and wearing a cooking pot on his head. "I'll come with you, Mulan," he said. "I'll protect you. I'll make my dragon face and they'll all run away." The boy opened his eyes wide, showed his teeth, and stretched his fingers out like claws.

Mulan gently said, "I know you would, brother. But if you scared them all away with your terrible dragon face, there would be no one left for our soldiers to fight. How could they win honor for their families then?"

The little boy nodded solemnly.

Mulan bid her parents goodbye. She mounted her horse and galloped away. She did not look back.

2. IN THE SHADOW OF BLACK MOUNTAIN

Astride her copper-colored horse, Mulan sped like a comet through the night. In the morning, she reached the army camp at the foot of Black Mountain. She marched up to the captain and told him the village she came from. "Your name?" he asked, thumbing through the lists.

Mulan gave her father's name.

"Very well," said the captain, "your family will be checked off. Make camp wherever you wish. We ride out in the morning."

Mulan breathed a sigh of relief as she spread her bedroll by the river. "They are safe," she murmured to her horse. "Somewhere along this river, my family is safe."

The girl sat down on her bedroll. The only sounds were the sad cries of birds and the rough laughter of soldiers. Mulan bit her lip. She could not hear father's voice or her mother's slippers shuffling along the floor. She wished to hear her little brother roar just once more. Tears welled in her eyes.

Angrily, she shook her head. "Little sisters have no place in an army camp," she muttered. "I promised I would be the older brother, so Older Brother I shall be!"

She pulled her sword out of her belt, ran to the river, and tore off her helmet. Thick waves of smooth, shiny hair cascaded down her back. Again and again the sharp blade flashed in the moonlight, until the lovely black tresses were nothing but a dark pile in the mud.

Mulan ran her hand over her nearly bald head. Then, for the last time, she cried. But the river ran by, murmuring, "Shh, shh," and finally Mulan fell asleep.

The captain was true to his word. In the morning, the company rode out to face the fierce warriors on the plain.

Vultures shrieked overhead. The wind stilled, and the air grew heavy. The horses swished their tails. Then a dark cloud appeared on the horizon. The cloud grew larger as it rolled toward Mulan and the army. But this was no storm. It was the terrible shadow of the enemy.

The two armies faced each other on the plain. Mulan could see the warriors' faces. They had darker skin and different uniforms, but surely they, too, had mothers, fathers, and little brothers who roared. "Who are these people?" Mulan wondered. "Will any of us ever see our families again?"

But then the drums were sounded, the battle cry filled her ears, and war sang in her veins. Without hesitation, Mulan spurred her horse and thundered into the fray.

Those who saw Mulan fight that day whispered, "That soldier is a tiger. His sword is ten thousand silver claws!"

After the battle, the soldiers invited Mulan to eat with them. Her modesty and kind ways earned her much respect and many friends.

In battle after battle, Mulan's bravery inspired fear in her enemies and awe in her comrades. And so she rose through the ranks like a dragon through the clouds until, at last, Mulan was made a general.

Ten winters had blasted the land with their freezing breath when General Mulan marshaled her tired troops. "We have fought for a thousand years," she said to her soldiers, "but now our enemy flees before us. He hopes to hide in the mountains and regain his strength. He thinks we are too lazy, too clumsy to chase him in winter."

Mulan paused, and then said firmly, "Someday this war will be over. Our names and deeds will be forgotten. But our glory will shine in the face of every man, woman, and child who loves our country and calls it by name, from now until the end of time. Follow me, and we shall end this war, and see the new dawn of our golden kingdom as the sun shines forth in spring!"

The soldiers cheered and readied their horses. As fast as flying, General Mulan hunted the enemy. The icy wind never blew without carrying the rattle of her soldiers' shields, and the sun never rose without reflecting off of Mulan's armor.

At last, when the first trees burst into leaf, General Mulan stood at the top of a mountain with her army behind her and looked at her country, free once more. In the distance, she spied the river, and thought, "Again, they are safe. Somewhere down that river, my family is safe."

She turned to her soldiers. "We have won," she said, and plunged her father's sword into the ground.

Up and down the northern border, every soldier, captain, and general celebrated their victory. But as General Mulan sat down to eat with her troops, a man approached her. His face was hidden in shadows, but he wore the insignia of the Emperor.

"General," his voice rumbled, "you have been summoned."

3. MULAN'S RETURN

Mulan knelt before the Emperor's throne. "He knows I am a woman," she thought. "I have disgraced my country and myself by lying, and now he will have me killed."

The Emperor studied Mulan. "Who is this general whom I have heard so much about, who is at once both fierce and gentle, wise and playful, mighty and humble?" he wondered. He looked at Mulan's face. It was weather-beaten and wrinkled now, but there was something about it, something….

The Emperor's jaw dropped slightly. He covered his mouth with his hand and pretended to yawn, but nothing could disguise the amazement in his eyes.

The Emperor coughed a little and then said, "General." Mulan squared her shoulders, ready for death. "We are indebted to you for your brave service to our country. We offer you anything you wish for your reward. Name your heart's desire, and it shall be yours."

Mulan replied, "To serve my country and my people is my heart's desire. I have need of nothing more."

The Emperor raised his eyebrows and thought. Then he said, "We serve best when we serve for the sake of those we love. Go home, General. But say you will return when we have need of you again."

"But think my name," said Mulan, "and I shall come."

The Emperor gave Mulan the finest horse from his stables, and sent a magnificent honor guard to accompany her home.

After a long journey, Mulan and her soldiers rode up the dusty lane where she and her brother had played so many years ago. She dismounted and walked to the door of her home. For a moment, she could not bring herself to knock. Then, just as she raised her hand, her mother opened the door.

Mother and daughter looked at each other. This day, both women's eyes filled with tears of joy. "I'm home," whispered Mulan.

Mulan's father hobbled out the door. Mulan tried to give him back his sword, but he said, "No, no, it's yours. Keep it. You earned it."

Mulan's little brother, grown now, almost a man, bowed to Mulan. She shook her head, smiled at him, and mouthed the word, ROAR! The young man blushed and grinned, then ran to the marketplace to fetch food and drink for a great celebration.

Mulan entered her house and opened the door to her room. Nothing had been moved. The great general sighed and began unlacing her armor. Carefully, she dressed herself in soft, colorful silks, and wove flowers into her hair. She took a long look at herself in the mirror—and laughed. Then, with her mother and father beside her, she went back out to face her soldiers.

The men gasped. "Where is our general? Who are you?"

"I am their daughter. I am your general. I am Mulan," she said.

The soldiers shook their heads, amazed. Mulan's parents beamed with pride. Together, they went inside to a marvelous feast to celebrate Mulan, their valiant daughter, Mulan, their wise general—Mulan, their hero for a thousand years.

St. George and the Dragon

retold by J. Berg Esenwein and Marietta Stockard

Long ago, when the knights lived in the land, there was one knight whose name was Sir George. He was not only braver than all the rest, but he was so noble, kind, and good that the people came to call him Saint George.

No robbers ever dared to trouble the people who lived near his castle, and all the wild animals were driven away, so the little children could play even in the woods without being afraid.

One day St. George rode throughout the country. Everywhere he saw the men busy at their work in the fields, the women singing at work in their homes, and the little children shouting at their play.

"These people are all safe and happy; they need me no more," said St. George.

"But somewhere perhaps there is trouble and fear. There may be some place where little children cannot play in safety, some woman may have been carried away from her home—perhaps there are even dragons left to be slain. Tomorrow I shall ride away and never stop until I find work that only a knight can do."

Early the next morning St. George put on his helmet and all his shining armor, and fastened his sword at his side. Then he mounted his great white horse and rode out from his castle gate. Down the steep, rough road he went, sitting straight and tall, and looking brave and strong as a knight should look.

On through the little village at the foot of the hill and out across the country he rode. Everywhere he saw rich fields filled with waving grain. Everywhere there was peace and plenty.

He rode on and on until at last he came into a part of the country he had never seen before. He noticed that there were no men working in the fields. The houses he passed stood silent and empty. The grass along the roadside was scorched as if a fire had passed over it. A field of wheat was all trampled and burned.

St. George drew up his horse and looked carefully about him. Everywhere there was silence and desolation. "What dreadful thing has driven all the people from their homes? I must find out, and give them help if I can," he said.

But there was no one to ask, so St. George rode forward until at last far in the distance he saw the walls of a city. "There I shall surely find someone who can tell me the cause of all this," he said, so he rode more swiftly toward the city.

Just then the great gate opened and St. George saw crowds of people standing inside the wall. Some of them were weeping, and all of them seemed afraid. As St. George watched, he saw a beautiful maiden dressed in white, with a girdle of scarlet about her waist, pass through the gate alone. The gate clanged shut and the maiden walked along the road, weeping bitterly. She did not see St. George, who was riding quickly toward her.

"Maiden, why do you weep?" he asked as he reached her side.

She looked up at St. George sitting there on his horse, so straight and tall and beautiful. "Oh, Sir Knight!" she cried, "ride quickly from this place. You know not the danger you are in!"

"Danger!" said St. George. "Do you think a knight would flee from danger? Besides, you, a fair girl, are here alone. Think you a knight would leave you or any woman so? Tell me your trouble that I may help you."

"No! No!" she cried, "hasten away. You would only lose your life. There is a terrible dragon near. He may come at any moment. One breath would destroy you if he found you here. Go! Go quickly!"

"Tell me more of this," said St. George sternly. "Why are you here alone to meet this dragon? Are there no men left in yon city?"

"Oh," said the maiden, "my father, the King, is old and feeble. He has only me to help him take care of his people.

This terrible dragon has driven them from their homes, carried away their cattle, and ruined their crops. They have all come within the walls of the city for safety. For weeks now the dragon has come to the very gates of the city. We have been forced to give him two sheep each day for his breakfast.

"Yesterday there were no sheep left to give, so he said that unless a young maiden were given him today he would break down the walls and destroy the city. The people cried to my father to save them, but he could do nothing. I am going to give myself to the dragon. Perhaps if he has me, the Princess, he may spare our people."

"Lead the way, brave Princess. Show me where this monster may be found."

When the Princess saw St. George's flashing eyes and great, strong arm as he drew forth his sword, she felt afraid no more. Turning, she led the way to a shining pool.

"There's where he stays," she whispered. "See, the water moves. He is waking."

St. George saw the head of the dragon lifted from the pool. Fold on fold, he rose from the water. When he saw St. George he gave a roar of rage and plunged toward him. The smoke and flames flew from his nostrils, and he opened his great jaws as if to swallow both the knight and his horse.

St. George shouted and, waving his sword above his head, rode at the dragon. Quick and hard came the blows from St. George's sword. It was a terrible battle.

At last the dragon was wounded. He roared with pain and plunged at St. George, opening his great mouth close to the brave knight's head.

St. George looked carefully, then struck with all his strength straight down through the dragon's throat. The creature fell at the horse's feet—dead.

Then St. George shouted for joy at his victory. He called to the Princess. She came and stood beside him.

"Give me the girdle from about your waist, O Princess," said St. George.

The Princess gave him her girdle and St. George bound it around the dragon's neck. They pulled the dragon after them by that little silken ribbon back to the city, for all the people to see that the dragon would never harm them again.

When they saw St. George bringing the Princess back in safety and knew that the dragon was slain, they threw open the gates of the city and sent up great shouts of joy.

The King heard them and came out from his palace to see why the people were shouting. When he saw his daughter safe he was the happiest of them all.

"O brave Knight," he said, "I am old and weak. Stay here and help me guard my people from harm."

"I'll stay as long as ever you have need of me," St. George answered.

So he lived in the palace and helped the old King take care of his people, and when the old King died, St. George was made King in his stead. The people felt happy and safe so long as they had such a brave and good man for their King.

THE LAST OF THE DRAGONS
by E. Nesbit

Of course you know that dragons were once as common as buses are now, and almost as dangerous. But as every well-brought-up prince was expected to kill a dragon and rescue a princess, the dragons grew fewer and fewer, till it was often quite hard for a princess to find a dragon to be rescued from. And at last there were no more dragons in France and no more dragons in Germany, or Spain, or Italy, or Russia. There were some left in China, and are still, but they are cold and bronzy, and there never were any in America.

But the last real live dragon left was in England. That was a very long time ago, before what you call English history began. The dragon lived in Cornwall in the big, dark caves amidst the rocks, and a very fine big dragon it was, quite seventy feet long from the tip of its fearful snout to the end of its terrible tail. It breathed fire and smoke. And it rattled when it walked, because its scales were made of iron. Its wings were like half-umbrellas—or like bat's wings, only several thousand times bigger. Everyone was very frightened of it, and well they might be.

Now the King of Cornwall had one daughter, and when she was sixteen she would have to go and face the dragon. It would not eat her, of course, because a prince would come and rescue her. But the Princess could not help thinking it would be much pleasanter to have nothing to do with the dragon at all—not even be rescued from him.

"All the princes I know are such very silly boys," she told her father. "Why must I be rescued by a prince?"

"It's always done, my dear," said the King, taking his crown off and putting it on the grass. They were alone in the garden, and even kings must unbend sometimes.

"Father, darling," said the Princess presently, when she had made a daisy chain and put it on the King's head where the crown ought to have been. "Father, darling, couldn't we tie up one of the silly little princes for the dragon to look at— and then I could go and kill the dragon and rescue the prince? I fence much better than any of the princes we know."

"What an unladylike idea!" said the King. Then he put his crown on again, for he saw the Prime Minister coming with a basket of new bills for him to sign. "Dismiss the thought, my child. I rescued your mother from a dragon, and we don't want to set yourself up above her, I should hope?"

"But this is the last dragon. It is different from all other dragons."

"How?" asked the King.

"Because it is the last," said the Princess. And she went off to her fencing lesson, with which she took great pains. She took great pains with all her lessons, for she could not give up the idea of fighting the dragon. She took such pains that she became the strongest and boldest and most skillful and most sensible princess in Europe. She had always been the prettiest and nicest.

And the days and years went by, till at last the day came that was the day before the Princess was to be rescued from the dragon. The Prince who was to do this deed of valor was a pale prince, with large eyes and a head full of mathematics and philosophy, but he had unfortunately neglected his fencing lessons. He was to stay the night at the palace, and there was a banquet.

After supper the Princess sent her pet parrot to the Prince with a note. It said: "Please, Prince, come to the terrace. I want to talk to you without anybody else hearing. —The Princess."

So, of course, he went. He saw her gown of silver a long way off, shining among the shadows of the trees like water in starlight. And when he came quite close to her he said, "Princess, at your service," and bent his cloth-of-gold-covered knee and put his hand on his cloth-of-gold-covered heart.

"Do you think," said the Princess earnestly, "that you will be able to kill the dragon?"

"I will kill the dragon," said the Prince firmly, "or perish in the attempt."

"It's no use your perishing," said the Princess.

"It's the least I can do," said the Prince.

"What I'm afraid of is that it'll be the most you can do," said the Princess.

"It's the only thing I can do," said he, "unless I kill the dragon."

"Why you should do anything for me is what I can't see," said she.

"But I want to," he said. "You must know that I love you better than anything in the world."

When he said that, he looked so kind that the Princess began to like him a little.

"Look here," she said. "No one else will go out tomorrow. You know they tie me to a rock and leave me. And then everybody scurries home and puts up the shutters and keeps them shut till you ride through the town in triumph shouting that you've killed the dragon, and I ride on the horse behind you weeping for joy."

"I've heard that this is how it is done," said he.

"Well, do you love me well enough to come very quickly and set me free—and we'll fight the dragon together?"

"It wouldn't be safe for you."

"Much safer for both of us for me to be free, with a sword in my hand, than tied up and helpless. Do agree."

He could refuse her nothing. So he agreed. And the next day everything happened as she had said.

When he had cut the cords that tied her to the rocks, they stood on the lonely mountainside looking at each other.

"It seems to me," said the Prince, "that this ceremony could have been arranged without the dragon."

"Yes," said the Princess, "but since it has been arranged with the dragon—"

"It seems such a pity to kill the dragon—the last in the world," said the Prince.

"Well, then, let's not," said the Princess. "Let's tame it not to eat princesses but to eat out of their hands. They say everything can be tamed by kindness."

"Tamed by kindness means giving them things to eat," said the Prince. "Have you got anything to eat?"

She hadn't, but the Prince said that he had a few biscuits. "Breakfast was so very early," said he, "and I thought you might have felt faint after the fight."

"How clever," said the Princess, and they took a biscuit in each hand. And they looked here and they looked there, but never a dragon could they see.

"But here's its trail," said the Prince, and pointed to where the rock was scarred and scratched so that it made a track leading to the mouth of a dark cave. "Look, that's where it's dragged its brass tail and planted its steel claws."

"Let's not think how hard its tail and its claws are," said the Princess, "or I shall begin to be frightened. And I know you can't tame anything, even by kindness, if you're frightened of it. Come on. Now or never."

She caught the Prince's hand in hers, and they ran along the path toward the dark mouth of the cave. But they did not run into it. It really was so very dark.

So they stood outside, and the Prince shouted, "What ho! Dragon there! What ho within!" And from the cave they heard an answering voice and great clattering and creaking. It sounded as though a rather large factory were stretching itself and waking up out of its sleep.

The Prince and the Princess trembled, but they stood firm.

"Dragon! I say, dragon!" said the Princess. "Do come out and talk to us. We've brought you a present."

"Oh, yes, I know your presents," growled the dragon in a huge rumbling voice. "One of those precious princesses, I suppose? And I've got to come out and fight for her. Well, I tell you straight, I'm not going to do it. A fair fight I wouldn't say no to—a fair fight and no favor—but one of these put-up fights where you've got to lose—No. So I tell you. If I wanted a princess, I'd come and take her, in my own time. But I don't. What do you suppose I'd do with her if I had her?"

"Eat her, wouldn't you?" said the Princess in a voice that trembled a little.

"Eat a fiddlestick end," said the dragon very rudely. "I wouldn't touch the horrid thing."

The Princess's voice grew firmer. "Do you like biscuits?" she asked.

"No," growled the dragon.

"Not the nice little expensive ones with sugar on the top?"

"No," growled the dragon.

"Then what do you like?" asked the Prince.

"You go away and don't bother me," growled the dragon. They heard it turn over with a clang and clatter.

The Prince and Princess looked at each other. What were they to do? It was no use going home and telling the King that the dragon didn't want princesses. He wouldn't believe it.

And they couldn't go into the cave and kill the dragon. Indeed, unless it attacked the Princess, it did not seem fair to kill it at all.

"It must like something," whispered the Princess, and she called out in a voice as sweet as honey and sugar cane, "Dragon! Dragon dear!"

"WHAT?" shouted the dragon coming towards them through the darkness of the cave.

The Princess shivered, and said in a very small voice, "Dragon—dragon dear!"

And then the dragon came out. The Prince drew his sword and the Princess drew hers—the beautiful silver-handled one that the Prince had brought in his car. But they did not attack. They moved slowly back as the dragon came out, all the vast scaly length of it, and lay along the rock, its great wings half spread and its golden sheen gleaming and sparkling in the sun. At last they could retreat no farther—the dark rock behind them stopped their way—and with their backs to the rock they stood with swords in hand and waited.

The dragon drew nearer and nearer. Now they could see that it was not breathing fire and smoke as they had expected. It came crawling slowly toward them, wriggling a little as a puppy does when it wants to play and isn't quite sure whether you're angry with it.

And they saw that great tears were rolling down its cheeks.

"Whatever's the matter?" said the Prince.

"Nobody," sobbed the dragon, "ever called me 'dear' before!"

"Don't cry, dragon dear," said the Princess. "We'll call you 'dear' as often as you like. We want to tame you."

"I am tame," said the dragon. "That's just it. That's what nobody but you has ever found out. I'm so tame that I'd eat out of your hands."

"Eat what, dragon dear?" said the Princess. "Not biscuits?" The dragon slowly shook its heavy head.

"Not biscuits?" said the Princess tenderly. "What then, dragon dear?"

"Your kindness quite undragons me," it said. "No one has ever asked any of us what we like to eat. Always offering us princesses and then rescuing them. And never once asking, 'What would you like to drink the King's health with?' Cruel hard I call it," and it wept again.

"But what would you like to drink our health with?" said the Prince. "We're going to be married today, aren't we, Princess?"

She said that she supposed so.

"What shall I take to drink your health with?" asked the dragon. "Ah, you're something like a gentleman, you are, sir. I don't mind if I do, sir. I'll be proud to drink your and your good lady's health with a tiny drop of—" Its voice faltered. "To

think of you asking me so friendly-like," it said. "Yes, sir, just a tiny drop of gasoline. That's what does a dragon good, sir—"

"I've lots in the car," said the Prince, and he was off down the mountain like a flash. He was a good judge of character, and he knew that with this dragon the Princess would be safe.

"If I might be so bold," said the dragon, "while the gentleman's away—p'raps just to pass the time you'd be so kind as to call me 'dear' again. And if you'd shake claws with a poor old dragon that's never been anybody's enemy but its own—well, the last of the dragons'll be the proudest dragon there's ever been since the first of them."

It held out an enormous paw, and the great steel hooks that were its claws closed over the Princess's hand so softly she hardly felt them.

And so the Prince and Princess went back to the palace in triumph, the dragon following them like a pet dog. And all through the wedding festivities no one drank more earnestly to the happiness of the bride and bridegroom than the Princess's pet dragon, whom she had at once named Fido.

And when the happy pair were settled in their own kingdom, Fido came to them and begged to be allowed to make itself useful. "There must be some little thing I can do," it said, rattling its wings and stretching its claws.

So the Prince had a special saddle made for it—very long it was—and one hundred and fifty seats were fitted to this. And the dragon, whose greatest pleasure was now to give pleasure to others, delighted in taking parties of children to the seaside. It flew through the air quite easily with its hundred and fifty little passengers, and would lie on the sand patiently waiting till they were ready to return. The children were very fond of it and used to call it "dear," a word which never failed to bring tears of affection and gratitude to its eyes.

So it lived, useful and respected, till just the other day when someone happened to say, in its hearing, that dragons were out of date, now that so much new machinery had come. This so distressed the dragon that it asked the Prince to change it into something less old-fashioned, and the kindly monarch at once changed it into a modern machine. The dragon, indeed, became the first airplane.

ROBIN HOOD AND ALLIN-A-DALE
retold by James Baldwin

In the long-ago days of King Richard and King John, there were many great woods in England. The most famous of these was Sherwood Forest, where the king often went to hunt deer. In this forest there lived a band of daring men called outlaws.

They had done something that was against the laws of the land, and had been forced to hide themselves in the woods to save their lives. There they spent their time in roaming about among the trees, in hunting the king's deer, and in robbing rich travelers that came their way.

There were nearly a hundred of these outlaws, and their leader was a bold fellow called Robin Hood. They were dressed in suits of green, and armed with bows and arrows. Sometimes they carried long wooden lances and swords, which they knew how to handle well. Whenever they had taken anything, it was brought and laid at the feet of Robin Hood, whom they called their king. He then divided it fairly among them, giving to each man his just share.

Robin never allowed his men to harm anybody but the rich men who lived in great houses and did no work. He was always kind to the poor, and he often sent help to them, and for that reason the common people looked upon him as their friend.

Long after he was dead, men liked to talk about his deeds. Some praised him, and some blamed him. He was indeed, a rough, lawless fellow, but at that time, people did not think of right and wrong as they do now.

A great many songs were made up about Robin Hood, and these songs were sung in the cottages and huts all over the land for hundreds of years afterward.

Here is a little story that is told in one of those songs.

Robin Hood was standing one day under a green tree by the roadside. While listening to the birds among the leaves, he saw a young man passing by. This young man was dressed in a fine suit of red cloth, and, as he tripped gaily along the road, he seemed to be as happy as the day.

"I will not trouble him," said Robin Hood, "for I think he is on the way to his wedding."

The next day Robin stood in the same place. He had not been there long when he saw the same young man coming down the road. But he did not seem to be so happy this time. He had left his scarlet coat at home, and at every step he sighed and groaned.

"Ah, the sad day!" he kept saying to himself.

Robin Hood stepped out from under the tree and said, "I say, young man! Have you any money to spare for my merry men and me?"

" I have nothing at all," said the young man, "but five shillings and a ring."

"A gold ring?" asked Robin Hood. "A gold ring?"

"Yes," said the young man, "it is a gold ring. Here it is."

"I have kept it these seven years," said the young man. "I have kept it to give to my bride on our own wedding day. We were going to be married yesterday. But her father has promised her to a rich old man whom she has never seen. And now my heart is broken."

"What is your name?" asked Robin.

"My name is Allin-a-Dale," said the young man.

"What will you give me in gold or fee," said Robin, "if I will help you win your bride again in spite of the rich old man to whom she has been promised?"

"I have no money," said Allin, "but I will promise to be your servant."

"How many miles is it to the place where the maiden lives?" asked Robin.

"It is not far," said Allin. "But she is to be married this very day, and the church is five miles away."

Then Robin made haste to dress himself as a harper. And in the afternoon he stood in the door of the church.

"Who are you?" said the bishop, "and what are you doing here?"

"I am a bold harper," said Robin, "the best in the North Country."

"I am glad you have come," said the bishop kindly. "There is no music I like so well as that of the harp. Come in, and play for us."

"I will go in," said Robin Hood, "but I will not give you any music until I see the bride and bridegroom."

Just then an old man came in. He was dressed in rich clothing, but was bent with age, and was feeble and gray. By his side walked a fair young girl. Her cheeks were very pale, and her eyes were full of tears.

"This is no match," said Robin. "Let the bride choose for herself."

Then he put his horn to his lips and blew three times. The very next minute, four and twenty men, all dressed in green,

and carrying long bows in their hands, came running across the fields. As they marched into the church all in a row, the foremost among them was Allin-a-Dale.

"Now whom do you choose?" said Robin to the maiden.

"I choose Allin-a-Dale," she said, blushing.

"Then Allin-a-Dale you shall have," said Robin, "and he that takes you from Allin-a-Dale shall find that he has Robin Hood to deal with."

And so the fair maiden and Allin-a-Dale were married then and there, and the rich old man went home in a great rage.

And, as the old song says,

> *And thus having ended this merry wedding,*
> *The bride looked like a queen;*
> *And so they returned to the merry green wood,*
> *Amongst the leaves so green.*

ROBIN HOOD AND THE GOLDEN ARROW

by Eva March Tappan

1

"It's a fine thing to be a great man," said the Sheriff of Nottingham, "but we have our troubles."

"Yes, we do," agreed the sheriff's wife. "Our new clothes came too late to wear to the Lord Mayor's feast. I'm sure that the stone house next door will be larger than ours. What's more, there's that little old woman who lives in the thatched cottage by the forest, and she wears a cloak that's finer than mine. I know it is, for she had the boldness to walk into the church before me and I felt of it when she came in the door. Oh, it's grand to be great folk, as you say, but even great folk have their worries."

"It's worse than a woman's cloak that worries me," replied the sheriff. "It's the bold and sturdy thief that lives in the forest, who's wearing my life away. He's robbed from all the rich folk in town. Why, I have no doubt that he'd even rob me if he got the chance, but I look out for him. It takes a wise man to catch me asleep."

"Indeed it does," agreed his wife.

"If the fine cloak troubles you, how much do you think the thief who gave it to that old woman troubles me? He's giving fine clothes to poor folk. He's putting new thatches on their roofs. He's paying their rent for them, and carrying them loads of wood when they ought to be out in the forest picking up sticks for themselves. They'll think they're as good as we great folk before long. I have no doubt that he's already given them white bread and wine instead of oatcake and water."

"You can not catch this thief?"

"No more than you can catch the wind. He's here and he's there. If you get him into prison, he finds a way out. I fear the king will think I'm not trying to catch him. I believe I'll go to London and ask the king how he thinks I ought to catch him."

"Well, now, I wouldn't do that," said the sheriff's wife. "I know that when Jane comes to me and tells me she's having trouble making the butter, I say, 'Jane, you've got the churn, haven't you? And the cream?' And when she says 'Yes,' I say to her, 'You have the churn and the cream, so it's your part to make the butter.'"

So said the sheriff's wife, but the sheriff thought, "My wife may talk, but I'm sure she was glad to know Jane was trying to make the butter and was worried enough to ask about it. I think the king would be pleased to know that I'm troubled about Robin Hood, and that I'm not forgetting my business. All men like others to ask them for advice. And for all his crown and throne, the king, too, is just a man."

The sheriff put on his best clothes, mounted his horse, and set off for London. All the way, he planned what he would say to the king, and imagined how the great king would thank him for caring so much about a single thief.

The sheriff reached the castle. He told the king of Robin Hood's bold deeds, and asked for his advice. The king said, "My good servant, you are the Lord High Sheriff of Nottingham, are you not?"

"Yes, my Lord King," answered the sheriff.

"And there is no need of a new law against robbery?"

"No, my Lord King."

"Then you have come to London only to ask my advice concerning the man that troubles you?"

"Yes, my Lord King."

"Then the very best advice I can give you is to go home and catch the thief. My Lord Chamberlain, see to it that the High Sheriff of Nottingham has proper refreshment and is shown all courtesy."

The sheriff bowed and backed out of the audience-room. When he was gone, the king and queen exchanged small smiles, and the queen said, "You did that quite well, dear."

The sheriff set out for Nottingham. He was surely the happiest man to leave London that day, and he surely thought he was the greatest. But when he repeated the king's advice to his wife, she frowned and looked grave.

"It isn't every man that is great enough to ask the king for advice," he said, trying to coax a smile out of her.

"It isn't every man that is foolish enough," she snapped.

"What?" cried the sheriff.

The sheriff's wife explained that the king had not given him one word of advice, but had only made fun of him. "And now you must catch Robin Hood," she said, "or I fear in another year, we'll have to leave this stone house, and another man will be the Sheriff of Nottingham."

The sheriff was thoroughly humbled and terribly frightened.

"Whatever shall I do? Will you help me?" he begged. "Your wit is keener than mine. Can't you devise some trick to catch Robin Hood? If you do, I will send to Flanders over the sea, and buy you the finest cloak that can be had for money."

""I'll think about it," she answered loftily, "and if my own wit gives out, why, I can go up to London and ask the king."

2

The next morning, the sheriff's wife woke her husband at the first crowing of the cock.

"I've thought of something," said she, "and if you do exactly as I tell you, and don't wander off into something you think is just as good, you will catch Robin Hood."

The sheriff promised he would do as she said, so she continued, "Now, who are the best archers in the North Country?"

"Why, Robin Hood and his men, of course," answered the sheriff.

"Did you ever know an archer that did not want to show his skill?"

"No," replied the sheriff, "but what has that to do with anything?"

The sheriff's wife shook her head. "Why, I should think a bat would see. Send notice all through all the country round and proclaim a shooting match. Offer a golden arrow or a silver bow as a prize, and you will see Robin Hood and his merry men soon enough."

"But how will I know them?" asked the sheriff helplessly. "Surely, they'll all be in disguise."

"I do believe you are still asleep. If Robin Hood and his men are the best shots, simply keep fast hold of the best shots, and you will have Robin and his men."

The sheriff was delighted. "You are the wisest woman in Nottingham," he said. "I'll send for that cloak today. And when I deliver Robin Hood into the hands of the king,

I shall send to France and buy you the finest satin gown in all the country."

That very day, the sheriff sent the criers round the North Country. They rang the bells and cried, "Hear ye, hear ye! A shooting match will be held on Nottingham Green, on Midsummer's Day, in the afternoon. The Lord High Sheriff of Nottingham has offered for the prize a golden arrow. Hear ye, hear ye!"

Of course, the criers would not enter the tangle of Sherwood Forest, but there were people enough to carry the great news to Robin and his men.

"Make ye ready, my merry men all," he cried, "and we will go to Nottingham and have some sport."

Then a young man stepped forward, dressed all in Lincoln green. He said, "Master Robin, let us stay here in the greenwood. The match is a trick, meant to deliver us into the hands and prison of the Sheriff of Nottingham."

Robin was not pleased. "David of Doncaster," said he, "if I did not know you for the brave man you are, I would say that was the speech of a coward. How do you know better than any other that the match is a trick?"

Now in the sheriff's house was a pretty serving-maid, and it was she who had told him. But the young man feared Robin's anger if he knew, so he hung his head and said nothing.

"Let us go to the match," said Robin, "come what will of it. Little John, what say you?"

"Let us go, indeed, Robin," said Little John, "and if there is a trick, we'll meet it with another trick. We'll wear no Lincoln green, but one shall wear white, another red, another yellow, and another blue. We'll mix with the other men. No two of us shall stay together. And if among us we do not win the golden arrow, we are no true archers."

The men went from the tangled greenwood to the shooting match on Nottingham Green. No two went together, and when they mixed with the thousand other men, even Robin himself would have trouble picking them out. It was no wonder that the sheriff could not find them.

"Ah well," said he, "it will be easy enough to find them when the shooting begins. I'll watch for a little company that keeps to themselves, and I'll have my men ready to follow them."

To be sure, his wife had said, "Keep fast hold of the best shots," but when he thought it over, he decided, "Women know nothing about shooting. It is a man's business to understand such matters. I know well that a bowman does not always make his very best shot. Even Robin and his men may miss. But if I watch for a little group of men that keep by themselves, I'll have them."

3

The shooting began, but watch as he would, the sheriff could see no little group of men that kept by themselves, or were in any way different from the hundreds of other men trying for the golden arrow.

One man and then another shot. The crowd shouted and cheered.

"Good for the brown!"

"Blue jacket, blue jacket!"

"Yellow forever!"

"Green's the color!"

"Cheer for the white, the white!"

"The red has it! The red, the red!"

The man in red had made the best shot. He was called up
before the sheriff to receive the golden arrow. The sheriff was
sorely vexed at not being able to find Robin Hood. But he did
not forget to present the arrow to the winner with the
greatest pomp. Said the sheriff to the man in red, "You are
the hero of the North Country, good sir, and an honor to
every man that ever bent a bow. May your arrow always fly
true to its target."

Now, of course, the man in red was no other than Robin
Hood. He received the arrow, bowed to the sheriff, and
melted away into the crowd. He and his men went home to
the greenwood, each taking a different road. Not a one of
them was followed by the sheriff's men.

Robin and his men met at the edge of Sherwood Forest.
They were all merry and light of heart, except Robin. Even
with the golden arrow stuck in his belt, he looked sorry
and vexed.

"What is wrong, Robin?" asked Little John. "You won the
prize, and the proud sheriff himself called you the hero of the

North Country. What more can you ask? He never even guessed it was you."

"That is what grieves me," said Robin sadly, turning the golden arrow over and over in his hands, "The proud sheriff will never know it was I to whom he gave the golden arrow. I'd willingly give it back to him, and a hundred gold pieces with it, if only there was some way of letting him know to whom he made his fine speech."

"Robin," said Little John, "you took my advice before and found it good. Will you take it once more?"

"Speak on," said Robin, "speak on. Your wit is as quick as a woman's. If the proud sheriff had but borrowed a woman's wit to help him, he'd have put me in the deepest dungeon cell by now."

So Little John told Robin of his plan, and all the company laughed and made ready.

It took the sheriff some time to get home after the match, because so many people wished to tell him what a beautiful prize he had given and congratulate him on what a successful day it had been. He was surely the happiest man to leave Nottingham Green that day, and he surely thought he was the greatest.

But his wife had gone as soon as the shooting was over, and cooked the finest dinner that can be imagined. As the sheriff came up the steps, she met him in the doorway, as smiling as two May mornings.

"I have been thinking," she said, "that we would take the thousand pieces of gold the king offered as a reward and make our house as big as the house next door, and maybe a little bigger. Which cell did you put him in?"

"Put whom in?" demanded the sheriff a little shortly.

"Robin Hood, of course, the man in red that made the best shot of all."

"That was not Robin Hood," declared the sheriff. " I watched for him every minute."

For a moment, the sheriff's wife had nothing to say, a thing that did not often happen. While she stood staring into her husband's face, a group of monks came to the steps, with their hoods drawn low over their faces.

"Here is a purse we found on the road," one said. "We thought it best to return lost property to the Lord High Sheriff."

"Thank you, good sirs, thank you," replied the sheriff, taking the purse, "and, please, here is a donation to your monastery." The monk who had spoken took the gold piece the sheriff offered, flashed a bright smile at the sheriff's wife, and led his fellows on down the road.

The sheriff opened the purse, and took out an arrow, a piece of parchment, and a red hat. His knees turned to water as he read, "This arrow is from Robin Hood, in return for the golden one that the sheriff so courteously bestowed on him today."

THE HORSE OF POWER

retold by Arthur Ransome

1

Once upon a time, a strong and powerful Tsar ruled in a country far away. Among his servants was a young archer. This archer had a horse, a great horse with a broad chest, eyes like fire, and hoofs of iron. This was a horse of power, such a horse as belonged to the valiant heroes of long ago.

One day, the young archer rode through the forest on his horse of power. The trees were green and little blue flowers blossomed on the ground. Squirrels ran in the branches and hares darted through the undergrowth. But no birds sang.

The young archer rode along the forest path and listened for the singing of the birds, but the forest was silent. The only noises were the scratching of four-footed beasts, the dropping of fir cones, and the heavy stamping of the horse of power on the path.

"What has become of the birds?" said the young archer.

He had scarcely said this before he saw a big curving feather lying in the path before him. The feather was larger than a swan's, larger than an eagle's. It lay in the path, glittering like a flame in the sun. The feather was pure gold. Then he knew why there was no singing in the forest. The firebird had flown that way. The feather in the path before him was a feather from its burning breast.

The horse of power spoke and said, "Leave the golden feather where it lies. If you take it you will be sorry, and you will know the meaning of fear."

Still the brave young archer sat on the horse of power and looked at the golden feather. He wondered whether to take it or not. He had no wish to learn what it was to be afraid, but he thought, "If I take it and bring it to the Tsar, my master, he will be pleased. And he will not send me away with empty hands, for no tsar in the world has a feather from the burning breast of the firebird."

The more he thought, the more he wanted to carry the feather to the Tsar. In the end he did not listen to the words of the horse of power. He leaped from the saddle and picked up the golden feather of the firebird. Then he mounted his horse again and galloped back through the green forest till he came to the palace of the Tsar.

He went into the palace, and bowed before the Tsar and said, "O Tsar, I have brought you a feather of the firebird."

The Tsar looked gladly at the feather, and then at the young archer.

"Thank you," said he. "But if you have brought me a feather of the firebird, you will be able to bring me the bird itself. I should like to see it. A feather is not a fit gift to bring to the Tsar. Bring the bird itself, or, I swear by my sword, your head will no longer sit between your shoulders!"

The young archer bowed his head and went out. Bitterly he wept, for now he knew what it was to be afraid. He went out into the courtyard. The horse of power was waiting for him, tossing its head and stamping the ground.

"Master," said the horse of power, "why do you weep?"

"The Tsar has told me to bring him the firebird, and no man on earth can do that," said the young archer, and he bowed his head on his breast.

"I told you," said the horse of power, "that if you took the feather you would learn the meaning of fear. Well, do not be frightened yet, and do not weep. The trouble is not now; the trouble lies before you. Go to the Tsar and ask him to have a hundred sacks of maize scattered over the open field, and let this be done at midnight."

The young archer went back into the palace and begged the Tsar for this. And the Tsar ordered that at midnight a hundred sacks of maize should be scattered in the open field.

Next morning, at the first redness in the sky, the young archer rode out to the field on the horse of power. The ground was scattered all over with maize. In the middle of the field stood a great oak with spreading boughs. The young archer leaped to the ground, took off the saddle, and let loose the horse of power. Then he climbed up into the oak and hid himself among the leaves.

The sky grew red and gold, and the sun rose. Suddenly, there was a noise in the forest around the field. The trees shook, swayed, and almost fell. There was a mighty wind. The sea piled itself into waves with crests of foam, and the firebird came flying from the other side of the world. Huge and golden and flaming in the sun, it dropped down with open wings into the field, and began to eat the maize.

The horse of power wandered in the field. This way he went, and that, but always he came a little nearer to the firebird. Nearer and nearer came the horse. He came very close to the firebird, and then suddenly stepped on one of its spreading fiery wings and pressed it heavily to the ground. The bird struggled, flapping mightily with its fiery wings, but it could not get away.

The young archer slipped down from the tree and bound the firebird with three strong ropes. He swung the bird on his back, saddled the horse, and rode to the palace of the Tsar.

The young archer stood before the Tsar. His back was bent under the great weight of the firebird. Its broad wings hung on either side of him like fiery shields, and there was a trail of golden feathers on the floor. The young archer laid the magic bird at the foot of the Tsar's throne. The Tsar was glad, because since the beginning of the world no tsar had seen the firebird flung before him like a wild duck caught in a snare.

The Tsar looked at the firebird and laughed with pride. He lifted his eyes to the young archer and said: "As you have known how to take the firebird, you will know how to bring me the bride I desire. In the land of Never, on the very edge of the world, where the sun rises in flame from behind the sea, lives the Princess Vasilissa. I will marry none but her. Bring her to me, and I will reward you with silver and gold. But if you do not bring her, then, by my sword, your head will no longer sit between your shoulders!"

The young archer wept bitter tears. He went out into the courtyard where the horse of power was stamping the ground with its hoofs of iron and tossing its thick mane.

"Master, why do you weep?" asked the horse of power.

"The Tsar has ordered me to go to the land of Never, and to bring back the Princess Vasilissa."

"Do not weep and do not grieve. The trouble is not now; the trouble lies before you. Ask the Tsar for a silver tent with a golden roof. Have him prepare it with all kinds of food and drink."

The young archer asked the Tsar for this. The Tsar gave him a silver tent with silver hangings and a golden-embroidered roof, every kind of rich wine, and the tastiest of foods.

Then the young archer mounted the horse of power and rode off to the land of Never. On and on he rode, many days

and nights, and came at last to the edge of the world, where the red sun rises in flame from behind the deep blue sea.

On the shore of the sea the young archer reined in the horse of power. He shaded his eyes and looked out over the blue water. There was the Princess Vasilissa in a little silver boat, rowing with golden oars.

The young archer rode back a little way to where the sand ended and the green world began. There he loosed the horse to wander where he pleased, and to feed on the green grass. Then he set up the shining tent on the edge of the shore, where the green grass ended and the sand began. In the tent he set out the tasty dishes and the rich flagons of wine the Tsar had given him. Then he sat himself down to wait for Princess Vasilissa.

The Princess Vasilissa dipped her golden oars in the blue water, and the little silver boat moved lightly through the dancing waves. When she looked over to the edge of the world, she saw the tent standing silver and gold in the sun. She dipped her oars, and came nearer to see it better. The nearer she came, the fairer seemed the tent.

Princess Vasilissa rowed to the shore and grounded her little boat on the golden sand. She stepped out daintily and came up to the tent. She was a little frightened, and now and again she stopped and looked back to where the silver boat lay on the sand with the blue sea beyond.

At last, the Princess Vasilissa came up to the tent and looked in.

The young archer rose, bowed, and said, "Good day to you, Princess! Be so kind as to come in and take bread with me, and taste my wines."

And the Princess Vasilissa came into the tent and sat down with the young archer. She ate sweetmeats with him, and drank wine from the Tsar's golden goblet. But no sooner did the last drop trickle down her slender throat than her eyes closed against her will, once, twice, thrice.

"Ah me!" said the Princess, "it is as if the night itself had perched on my eyelids, yet it is only noon."

And the golden goblet dropped to the ground from her little fingers. She leaned back on a cushion and fell instantly asleep.

Quickly the young archer called to the horse of power. Lightly he lifted the Princess in his strong arms. Swiftly he leaped with her into the saddle. Like a feather she lay in the hollow of his left arm, and slept while the great horse thundered away from the land of Never.

When they came to the Tsar's palace, the young archer leaped from the horse of power and carried the Princess inside. Great was the joy of the Tsar; but it did not last for long.

"Go, sound the trumpets for our wedding," he said to his servants. "Let all the bells be rung."

The bells rang out and the trumpets sounded. At the noise of the horns and the ringing of the bells, the Princess Vasilissa woke and looked about her.

"What is this ringing of bells," said she, "and this noise of trumpets? And where, oh, where is the blue sea, and my little silver boat with its golden oars?" And the Princess put her hand to her eyes.

"The blue sea is far away," said the Tsar. "But for your little silver boat I give you a golden throne. The trumpets sound for our wedding, and the bells are ringing for our joy."

But the Princess turned her face away from the Tsar. There was no wonder in that, for he was old, and his eyes were not kind.

The Princess then looked with love at the young archer. There was no wonder in that either, for he was a young man fit to ride the horse of power.

The Tsar was angry with the Princess. But his anger was as useless as his joy.

"Princess," said he, "will you not marry me, and forget your blue sea and your silver boat?"

"In the middle of the deep blue sea lies a great stone," said the Princess. "Under that stone is hidden my wedding dress. If I cannot wear that dress I will marry nobody at all."

Instantly the Tsar turned to the young archer, who was waiting before the throne.

"Did you hear what the Princess said?" cried the Tsar. "Ride swiftly back to the land of Never. Bring back that dress, or, by my sword, your head will no longer sit between your shoulders!"

The young archer wept bitter tears, and went out into the courtyard, where the horse of power was waiting for him, champing its golden bit.

"Master, why do you weep?" asked the horse of power.

"The Tsar has ordered me to fetch the wedding dress of the Princess Vasilissa from the bottom of the deep blue sea. Worse still, the dress is wanted for the Tsar's wedding. But I love the Princess myself."

"What did I tell you?" said the horse of power. "I told you that there would be trouble if you picked up the firebird's feather. Well, do not be afraid. The trouble is not now; the trouble lies before you. Up! Into the saddle with you, and away for the wedding dress of the Princess!"

2

The young archer leaped into the saddle. The horse of power, with his thundering hoofs, carried him swiftly through the green forests and over the bare plains, till they came to the edge of the world, to the land of Never, where the red sun rises in flame from behind the deep blue sea. There they rested, at the very edge of the sea.

The young archer looked sadly over the wide waters. The horse of power did not look at the sea, but on the shore. This way and that it looked, and saw at last a huge lobster moving slowly, sideways, along the golden sand.

Nearer and nearer came the lobster. It was a giant, the tsar of all the lobsters. It moved slowly along the shore. The horse of power moved carefully, as if by accident, until it stood between the lobster and the sea. When the lobster came close by, the horse of power lifted an iron hoof and set it firmly on the lobster's tail.

"You will be the death of me!" screamed the lobster. The heavy foot of the horse of power was pressing his tail into the sand. "Let me live, and I will do whatever you ask of me."

"Very well," said the horse of power, "we will let you live." Slowly, he lifted his foot. "But this is what you shall do for us. In the middle of the blue sea lies a great stone, and under that stone is hidden the wedding dress of the Princess Vasilissa. Bring it here."

The lobster groaned with the pain in his tail. Then he called out in a voice that could be heard all over the deep blue sea. The sea began to stir. From all sides, thousands of lobsters made their way toward the bank. The tsar of all the lobsters gave them the order and sent them back into the sea. And the young archer sat on the horse of power and waited.

After a time, the sea stirred again. Thousands of lobsters came up onto the shore. They brought the golden casket with the wedding dress of the Princess. They had taken it from under the great stone that lay in the middle of the sea.

The tsar of all the lobsters raised himself on his bruised tail and gave the casket to the archer. Instantly the horse of power galloped back to the Tsar's palace, far, far away, on the other side of the green forests and beyond the treeless plains.

The young archer went into the palace and gave the casket into the hands of the Princess. He looked at her with sadness in his eyes. She looked at him with love. Then she went away into an inner chamber, and came back in her wedding dress. She looked fairer than spring itself.

Great was the joy of the Tsar. The wedding feast was made ready, and the bells rang, and flags waved above the palace.

The Tsar held out his hand to the Princess, and looked at her with his unkind eyes. But she would not take his hand.

"No," said she, "I will marry no one until the man who brought me here has been punished in boiling water."

Instantly the Tsar turned to his servants and ordered them to make a great fire. "Fill a great cauldron with water and set it on the fire," said he. "When the water is at its hottest, throw the archer into it. He must be punished for taking the Princess Vasilissa away from the land of Never."

There was no gratitude in the mind of that Tsar.

Swiftly the servants brought wood and made a mighty fire. On it they laid a huge cauldron of water. The fire raged. The water bubbled and seethed. They prepared to take the young archer and throw him into the cauldron.

"Oh, misery!" thought the young archer. "Why did I ever take the firebird's feather? Why did I not listen to the wise words of the horse of power?" Then he remembered the horse of power, and begged the Tsar, "Oh lord Tsar, I do not complain. I shall presently die in the heat of the water on the fire. Please let me see my horse once more before I die."

"Let him see his horse," said the Princess.

"Very well," said the Tsar. "Say good-bye to your horse, for you will not ride him again. But let your farewells be short, for we are waiting."

The young archer crossed the courtyard and came to the horse of power, who was scraping the ground with his iron hoofs.

"Farewell, my horse of power," said the young archer. "I should have listened to your words of wisdom. Now my end is come. Never again shall we race the wind between the earth and the sky."

"Why so?" said the horse of power.

"The Tsar has ordered me to be boiled to death. In a moment, they will throw me into the cauldron on the great fire."

"Fear not," said the horse of power. "The Princess Vasilissa has made him do this, and the end of these things is better than I thought. Go back. When they are ready to throw you in the cauldron, run boldly and leap into the boiling water."

The young archer went wandering back across the courtyard. The servants made ready to throw him in.

"Are you sure the water is boiling?" asked the Princess Vasilissa.

"It bubbles and seethes," said the servants.

"Let me see for myself," said the Princess. She went to the fire and waved her hand above the cauldron. Some say there was something in her hand, while some say there was not.

"It is boiling," said she. The servants laid hands on the young archer. But he shook them off, and ran and leaped boldly before them all into the very middle of the cauldron.

Twice he sank below the surface, spun round by the bubbles and foam of the boiling water. Then he leaped from the cauldron and stood before the Tsar and the Princess. He had become so handsome that all who saw cried aloud in wonder.

"Amazing!" cried the Tsar. As he looked at the handsome young man, he thought of his bent back, his gray beard, and his toothless gums. "I too will become young and handsome," he thought. He rose from his throne and clambered into the cauldron. Instantly, he vanished in a puff of steam.

And the end of the story? The people made the young archer their new Tsar. He married the Princess Vasilissa, and lived many years with her in love and good fellowship. And he built a golden stable for the horse of power, and never forgot what he owed him.

Favorites from Famous Books

from

THE PRINCE AND THE PAUPER
by Mark Twain

THE BIRTH OF THE PRINCE AND THE PAUPER

In the ancient city of London, on an autumn day in the sixteenth century, a boy was born to a poor family of the name of Canty, who did not want him.

On the same day another English child was born to a rich family of the name of Tudor, who did want him.

All England wanted him too. England had longed for him, and hoped for him, and prayed God for him. Now that he had really come, the people went nearly mad for joy. Everybody took a holiday. Rich and poor feasted and danced and sang.

By day, London was a sight to see. Gay banners waved from every balcony and housetop. By night, it was again a sight to see, with great bonfires at every corner, and revelers making merry around them.

There was no talk in all of England except of the new baby, Edward Tudor, Prince of Wales. The baby lay in silks and satins, not knowing that great lords and ladies were watching over him—and not caring, either.

But there was no talk about the other baby, Tom Canty, in his poor rags, except among the family of paupers whom he had just come to trouble with his presence.

Tom's Early Life

Let us skip a number of years.

London was a great town for that time. It had a hundred thousand inhabitants. Some think it had double that many.

The streets were narrow, crooked, and dirty, especially where Tom Canty lived, which was not far from London Bridge.

The house Tom's father lived in was up a foul little pocket called Offal Court, off Pudding Lane. It was small, decayed, and rickety. And it was packed full of poor families.

The Canty family lived in a room on the third floor. The mother and father had a bed in the corner. But Tom, his grandmother, and his two sisters, Bet and Nan, could sleep wherever they chose—on the floor.

Bet and Nan were twins, fifteen years old. They were good-hearted girls, unclean, clothed in rags, and deeply ignorant. Their mother was like them.

But the father and grandmother were a couple of fiends. They fought each other or anybody else who came in the way. They cursed and swore.

John Canty was a thief, and his mother a beggar. They made beggars of the children, but failed to make thieves of them.

In the house lived a good old priest, who used to take the children aside and secretly teach them the right ways. Father Andrew also taught Tom a little Latin, and how to read and write. He would have done the same with the girls, but they were afraid of the jeers of their friends.

When Tom came home empty handed at night, he knew his father would curse him and thrash him. Then his grandmother would do it all over again. He also knew that later in the night his mother would slip to him stealthily with any scrap or crust she had been able to save for him by going hungry herself.

Yet little Tom was not unhappy. He had a hard time, but he did not know it. It was the sort of time that all the Offal Court boys had, so he supposed it was the correct and comfortable thing.

Tom's Dreams

Tom's life went along well enough, especially in summer. He only begged just enough to save himself, for the laws against begging were strict and the punishments heavy. So he spent a good deal of time listening to good Father Andrew's charming old tales about giants and fairies, enchanted castles, and gorgeous kings and princes.

His head grew to be full of these wonderful things. Many a night, as he lay in the darkness, tired and hungry, he let his imagination wander. He soon forgot his pains as he pictured the charmed life of a pampered prince in a palace.

In time, one desire came to haunt him day and night—to see a real prince with his own eyes. He spoke of it once to some of his Offal Court comrades. But they made such fun of him that he was glad to keep his dream to himself after that.

He often read the priest's old books and got him to explain them. His dreamings and readings changed him. His dream-people were so fine that he began to feel sad about his shabby clothing, and to wish to be clean and better clothed.

By and by, Tom began to act like a prince. His speech and manners became ceremonious and courtly. In time, the other boys of Offal Court looked up to him with a wondering awe. He seemed to know so much! And he could do and say such marvelous things!

The boys told their elders about Tom's remarks and actions. And soon, full-grown people brought their problems to Tom, and were often astonished at the wit and wisdom of his advice.

Tom had become a hero to all who knew him, except his own family, who saw nothing in him.

After a while, Tom organized a royal court. He was the prince. His special comrades were guards, chamberlains, lords and ladies, and the royal family. Daily they acted out the affairs of the kingdom with great ceremony, as Tom, the mock prince, issued orders to his imaginary armies and navies.

Afterwards, he would go forth in his rags and beg a few farthings, eat his poor crust, stretch himself upon his handful of foul straw, and resume his grand imaginings in his dreams.

All night long he moved among great lords and ladies, in a blaze of light, breathing perfumes, drinking in delicious music. As the glittering crowd parted to make way for him, he answered with here a smile and there a nod of his princely head.

He awoke in the morning and looked upon the usual wretchedness about him. Then came bitterness, and heartbreak, and tears.

And still his desire to look just once upon a real prince grew, day by day, week by week, until at last it became the one passion of his life.

What happens to poor Tom Canty? Does he ever meet a real prince? Some day you can read Mark Twain's novel, The Prince and the Pauper, *to enjoy the whole story. For now, here follows a play based on the main events in the novel.*

THE PRINCE AND THE PAUPER
a play based on the novel by Mark Twain
dramatized by Elizabeth Brenner

Characters

NARRATOR

TOM CANTY, A POOR BOY WHO LOOKS LIKE THE PRINCE

PRINCE EDWARD, A YOUNG ENGLISH PRINCE

LORD ST. JOHN

EARL OF HERTFORD

ADVISORS TO THE KING AND PRINCE

JOHN CANTY, TOM'S FATHER

MOTHER, TOM'S MOTHER

GAMMER CANTY, TOM'S GRANDMOTHER

HUGO

RUFFLER

FRIENDS OF JOHN CANTY

TWO GUARDS

TWO WOMEN

TWO MEN

PAGE

COOK

GROOM

BUTLER

LORD

LADY

ATTENDANTS OF THE COURT

SCENE 1

NARRATOR: This play takes place in the early sixteenth century. The setting is outside the gate of Westminster Palace in London. Two guards march to their stations while a crowd moves in on both sides. The crowd is talking about the royal family.

1ST WOMAN: Perhaps the King himself will come outside today.

2ND WOMAN: You hope for too much. If only I could get a glimpse of the young Prince! They say he is very handsome.

1ST MAN: I hear the King is ill. He'll not show himself this afternoon.

2ND WOMAN: I saw the royal Princess only last Sunday. She grows more beautiful every day.

2ND MAN: Look out, young fellow. Standing there is not a safe occupation for the likes of you.

TOM (*Excitedly*): The Prince! I can see the Prince!

1ST GUARD: Mind your manners, you young beggar!

TOM: Let me go! Let me go!

1ST MAN (*Quickly*): Look, the Prince is here!

2ND MAN: The Prince has come out of the palace grounds!

PRINCE (*Indignantly*): Guards! How dare you treat a poor lad like that! How dare you use my father's lowest subjects so! Release him! Open the gates and let him in. Away with you! (*In a kindly voice*) Lad, you look tired and hungry; you have been ill-treated. Come with me.

NARRATOR: A few minutes later, we find ourselves in the chamber of the Prince. Tom is sitting at a table spread with all kinds of food. He looks at it with awe as he eats. The Prince walks about the room, talking to Tom.

PRINCE: Good. Now that I've dismissed my attendants, we can talk. What is your name?

TOM: Tom Canty, if it please you, sir.

PRINCE: 'Tis an odd name. Where do you live?

TOM: Offal Court, in the city, sir.

PRINCE: Offal Court! Another odd name. Have you parents?

TOM: I have two parents and Gammer Canty, my grandmother, besides. But I do not care so much for her, if I may say so, sir. I also have sisters, Nan and Bet.

PRINCE: Is your grandmother not kind to you?

TOM: She has, I fear, a wicked heart, and is not kind to me or to anyone else.

PRINCE: Does she mistreat you?

TOM: There are times when she beats me, sir.

PRINCE: Beats you—and you so frail and small. To the Tower with her!

TOM: Sir, you forget our low station. The Tower is only for great criminals.

PRINCE: So it is. I shall have to think of some other punishment for her. Is your father kind to you?

TOM: No, worse than my grandmother, sir, but my mother is good to me, as are my sisters.

PRINCE: Well, that is better! Tell me more about your life at Offal Court. What do you do for fun there?

TOM: Oh, we do have a good time there, except when we are hungry. There are Punch and Judy shows, and dancing monkeys!

PRINCE: Yes, yes, go on!

TOM: We boys of Offal Court have sparring matches and races, and in the summer we wade and swim in the canals and the river.

PRINCE: It would be worth my father's kingdom to enjoy that just once!

TOM: We dance and sing around the Maypole, and roll in the mud sometimes, too.

PRINCE: Oh, say no more! If only I could wear clothes like yours just once and run barefoot through mud—I think I would give up my crown for that!

TOM: If I could wear such fine clothes as yours just once—

PRINCE *(Quickly):* Would you really like that? Then it shall be. I'll call the servants to clear the table. While they do that, you and I will have time to go into the next room and exchange clothing. *(Calls)* Page!

PAGE: Yes, Your Highness?

PRINCE: Tell the First Groom of the Chamber, the Lord Chief Butler, and the Lord Head Cook to come and clear away this table.

PAGE: Yes, Your Highness.

PRINCE: Quickly, lad, follow me. Now's our chance. My attendants will be occupied and will not find us.

NARRATOR: A moment later, the royal servants enter and clear the dining table. While they are busy, Tom and the Prince leave the room. When the boys re-enter, they have exchanged clothes. They run over and stare first into the mirror, then at each other.

PRINCE: What do you make of this, Tom Canty?

TOM: Your worship, do not make me answer. It is not right that a person of my station say such a thing.

PRINCE: Then I will say it. You have the same hair, the same eyes, the same voice and manner, the same stature, the same face as I. Now that we have exchanged clothing, there's no one who could tell us apart. Where did you get that bruise on your hand?

TOM: It is nothing, sir. The poor guard at the gate—

PRINCE: That was a cruel thing to do. I'll speak to him at once. Do not move until I return. That is a command.

NARRATOR: The Prince, in Tom's clothing, goes to the main gate. The guards, thinking he is Tom, laugh and rudely push him into the street.

1ST GUARD: Away with you, beggar!

2ND GUARD: That's what you get for making trouble for us with the Prince, you pauper.

PRINCE: I am the Prince of Wales, and you will be hanged for laying a hand on me.

1ST GUARD (*Mockingly*): I salute your gracious Highness. (*Angrily*) Be off, you crazy rubbish! And you too, old man! What do you want?

JOHN CANTY: I want the lad. So there you are, Tom, out gawking at royalty and haven't begged a farthing for me, I warrant. If it be so, I'll break all the bones in your body, or I'm not John Canty.

PRINCE: So you're his father. Then you will fetch him away and restore me to the palace.

JOHN CANTY: His father? I am your father, and I'll pound that lesson into you, I will.

PRINCE: Do not joke or delay any longer. Take me to the King, my father, and he will make you rich. Believe me—I am indeed the Prince of Wales.

JOHN CANTY (*Astonished*): He's always had a fancy for royalty, and now he's gone stark mad. But mad or not, Gammer Canty and I will cure the likes of you.

SCENE 2

NARRATOR: John Canty drags the boy to his home, believing the Prince is his son Tom. The next day, at the palace, several lords come into the Prince's room, where a table is elaborately spread for dinner. Listen as the men talk together.

ST. JOHN: What do you think, Lord Hertford?

HERTFORD: It worries me, Lord St. John. The King is near his end and my nephew is mad—mad he will mount the throne, and mad he will remain. God protect England. She will need it!

ST. JOHN: But—have you no doubts as to—as to—

HERTFORD: Speak on—doubts as to what?

ST. JOHN: I am loath to say what is on my mind, and you so closely related to him, my lord. Beg pardon if I offend you, then, but seems it not to you that his manner and speech differ in some trifles from what they were before? He did not recognize his own father, and he insists that he is not the Prince!

HERTFORD: Peace, my lord, you utter treasonous words. Remember the King's command.

ST. JOHN (*Concerned*): True, true, I did forget myself. Yes, he must be the Prince. There could not be two in the land who look so much alike.

HERTFORD (*A little doubtfully*): An impostor would claim to be the Prince. Has there ever been an impostor who would deny this? No, this must be the Prince gone mad. We must help him all we can. Ah, it is the Lord Head Cook.

COOK: Everything is ready for the Prince's dinner.

ST. JOHN: Good. Call in the other attendants. Lord Hertford and I have a message from the King.

COOK: Yes, my lord.

HERTFORD: Lord St. John, I understand your questioning, but you must do all you can to hide your doubts. It is up to us to see him through this.

ST. JOHN: I'm sorry. I should not have even mentioned such thoughts.

HERTFORD: Lord Head Cook, are the others coming?

COOK: Yes, my lord.

NARRATOR: Three court attendants enter the room: the butler, the groom, and the page. They bow to Hertford and St. John.

HERTFORD: Good afternoon, gentlemen. We have called you here to relay a special message from His Majesty, the King. Word has reached him that there is talk in the palace that the Prince has gone mad. Lord St. John will read to you the declaration of the King. I shall fetch His Highness, the Prince.

ST. JOHN (*Reading*): "In the name of the King. Let none listen to this false and foolish matter, upon pain of death, nor discuss the same, nor carry it abroad. In the name of the King."

NARRATOR: Hertford and Tom enter. Tom sits at the table, awkward and ill at ease. He picks up the napkin and looks at it curiously, for he has never seen one before.

TOM: Please take this away. I am afraid it might get soiled.

HERTFORD: Your Highness had best retire early this evening, so you will not be tired for the city's banquet tomorrow.

TOM *(Surprised):* Banquet?

ST. JOHN: Your memory plays tricks on you, Your Highness. The King did promise a banquet in the city in your honor. Do you not recall?

TOM *(Still puzzled):* Yes, yes, I recall it now.

GROOM: What is the trouble, Your Highness?

TOM: I crave your help. My nose itches terribly. Pray, tell me—what is the royal custom in such a matter? I cannot bear it much longer.

GROOM: Lord Head Butler, what do you think? There has never been a case like this in all of England's history!

BUTLER: Alas, there is no hereditary Nose Scratcher!

COOK: What shall we do?

GROOM: What's to be done?

TOM: I hope I do not offend you, gentlemen, but I can wait no longer. I must scratch my nose. *(Scratches his nose)*

HERTFORD: Ah, here comes the page.

PAGE: Your Highness.

HERTFORD: Tell the page to rise, Your Highness.

TOM: Yes, Page. Rise and come forward.

PAGE: Your Highness, His Majesty the King requests the Great Seal. He says that it is most urgent.

TOM *(Bewildered):* The Great Seal? Methinks I have forgotten about that, too!

HERTFORD: The Great Seal which, during his illness, the King gave to you as a symbol of your approaching responsibilities.

TOM: Oh, yes, the Seal. Tell my father I have forgotten where I put it, but shall think upon it most carefully.

PAGE *(Hesitantly):* Yes, Your Majesty.

TOM: I am finished with my meal, my lord, and am in need of a rest.

HERTFORD: Lord Head Butler, pray clear away the table.

ST. JOHN: We shall leave you now, Your Highness, but shall return to remind you of your duties at the city's banquet.

TOM: Good, my lord. *(Pause)* I miss my mother, Nan, and Bet, though I cannot speak the same for my father and Gammer Canty. A city banquet in my honor! If I'm reminded of enough of the manners I've forgotten, I might begin to like it here! Ah! What book is this? "The E-ti-quette of the English Court." *(Happily)* This should be of great help!

SCENE 3

NARRATOR: A few weeks pass. Now we go to the Cantys' room in Offal Court. John Canty enters dragging the Prince with him.

JOHN CANTY *(Angrily):* Enough of your nonsense! This is your last chance to say who you really are or suffer the same beating as you had yesterday, and the day before, and the day before that one, too.

PRINCE: 'Tis ill breeding in such as you to command me to speak. I tell you now, as I told you before, I am Edward, Prince of Wales, and none other.

GAMMER *(Cackling):* So, 'tis still the Prince he is. Still too fancy for his own Gammer and his father, I warrant. 'Tis my turn to help him realize who he is. *(She laughs wickedly.)*

MOTHER: Oh, please do not hurt him today, husband. He is near ill with fatigue and hunger. My poor boy! Your foolish ideas have taken your wits away and are breaking my heart.

PRINCE: I tell you, your son is well and has not lost his wits, good dame. If you would let me go to the palace where he is, the King, my father, will return him to you.

MOTHER: The King your father! My child, do not say such things. They might mean death for you and the ruin of all of us. Call back your wandering memory and look upon me. Am I not your mother?

PRINCE (*Reluctantly*): I do not like to grieve you, kind madam, but you are not my mother.

GAMMER: 'Tis royalty he still is—too fine for his own family.

JOHN CANTY (*Sarcastically*): How dare you ladies stand in the Prince's presence? Upon your knees and do him reverence!

MOTHER: More rest and food will cure his madness. I'll fix him some soup with what scraps I can find. Come, Gammer, please help me.

GAMMER: I'll help you, but the soup will be for me and his father first.

JOHN CANTY: There'll be little rest for any of us unless you lower your royal self to begging soon. The rent is due tomorrow, and you have not yet begged a single penny.

PRINCE: Offend me not with your sordid matters. I tell you again, I am the King's son. Oh—who are these men?

JOHN CANTY: Ah, Hugo and Ruffler. Where have you been these many months? It is long since I have seen you.

HUGO: We've been in prison, that's where we've been. We were suspected of stealing a deer from the King's park. They kept us in prison a few months, but could not prove us guilty. They gave us a good whipping for causing them so much trouble, then set us free.

PRINCE: But why would they whip you if you were innocent? That is not just!

RUFFLER *(Laughing):* You young ones have such strange ideas. As if justice mattered in dear old England! We were lucky to escape with our lives; many innocents there be in prison, waiting to be hanged.

MOTHER: Here's some soup, Tom. 'Twill do you good to drink it.

PRINCE: Thank you, good madam. Your kindness will be remembered.

MOTHER: Oh, Tom, you talk as if your wits had left you. Please have the soup; perhaps it will restore your health and your memory.

JOHN CANTY: After you're finished bothering with "His Royal Highness," what about some food for the rest of your family?

MOTHER: Forgive me. I'll fix some for you now.

JOHN CANTY: Well, "Your Majesty," I hope that soup pleases your royal tongue.

PRINCE: I do not mean to offend your kind wife, sir, but I cannot eat this without the proper service.

JOHN CANTY: Is that so? Then you'll be starving, you will, before you find any "service" around here.

HUGO: The boy is ill, John Canty. Here's how you do it, Tom.

NARRATOR: Hugo takes the bowl in his hands and drinks a large portion of the soup.

PRINCE: I command you to stop!

RUFFLER: Come, Hugo, leave "His Majesty" to his dinner.

HUGO: But there is big news, John Canty. Word has got about that the King is dead!

NARRATOR: The Prince looks up, startled, then buries his head in his arms. His shoulders are shaking with sobs. John Canty looks at the Prince, shakes his head, and smiles.

JOHN CANTY: Little meaning that has for me. The new King is probably no better than his father.

RUFFLER: 'Tis heard that the young Prince will be crowned King before long. Then we shall see how much he cares for justice.

PRINCE *(Explosively):* Enough of this treason! I shall see that justice be done to you and to all the others who were ill-treated.

HUGO: Why, Tom Canty, who be you to talk such?

PRINCE *(Solemnly):* I am Edward the Sixth, King of England.

JOHN CANTY: Mates, my son is a dreamer, a fool, and stark mad. Mind him not. He thinks he is the King.

PRINCE *(Turning toward him):* I am the King, and as justice will be done these two men for their suffering, so will you be punished for treating me as you have.

JOHN CANTY: So you threaten me now! I shall go out with my friends here for a while and when I return, you'd best have begged the pennies for the rent or we'll see who's punishing whom around here. Come, Hugo, come, Ruffler, we'll tell the others you've returned. *(Mockingly)* Good day, Your Majesty.

HUGO AND RUFFLER: Good day, Your Majesty.

PRINCE: My father is dead and the pauper is an impostor. He must be more clever than I thought, or surely his rude manners would have betrayed him by now. I must get back to the palace, and I will.

Scene 4

NARRATOR: It is the day of the Coronation. At Westminster Abbey, Tom Canty is to be crowned King of England.

HERTFORD: A glorious day for all of England it is today, Lord St. John.

ST. JOHN: That it is, my lord—a day that will be long remembered.

HERTFORD: Did you mark how well the young King has been feeling and behaving of late?

ST. JOHN: Yes, I did. Perhaps his madness has left him at last.

NARRATOR: The sound of trumpets and drums is heard. The King is announced. Tom Canty, looking downcast, slowly approaches the throne.

HERTFORD: My liege, people see your downcast head and take it for a bad omen. Lift up your head and smile upon your subjects.

TOM: I am sorry, my lord, but as I came here, I saw my poor mother in the crowd. She recognized me, but I did not speak to her. I betrayed my own mother.

ST. JOHN: He has gone mad again!

HERTFORD: Your Majesty, we must proceed with the Coronation. Where is your kingly bearing?

TOM: I do not feel very kingly now, but let the ceremony begin.

NARRATOR: At this moment, the real prince forces his way into the room. He is dressed in Tom Canty's poor clothes, but he holds up his hand and speaks with authority.

PRINCE: Stop the ceremony at once!

LORD: Look there!

LADY: How did that pauper get in here?

LORD: I think he looks like the Prince.

PRINCE: I forbid you to set the crown of England upon that head. I am the King!

NARRATOR: Guards rush forward and seize the real prince for they do not recognize him. Tom steps down from the throne and speaks.

TOM (*Imperiously*): *Let him go! He is the King!*

HERTFORD: Mind not His Majesty. His malady is touching him again. Seize the pauper.

TOM: On your peril! Touch him not. He is the King! Your Majesty, let poor Tom Canty be first to swear his loyalty to you.

St. John: My lord, do you mark the resemblance between them?

Hertford: 'Tis an astonishing likeness! By your favor, sir, I desire to ask certain questions.

Prince: I will answer them, my lord.

Hertford: If you are the true King, tell me how many servants were at the palace when you left?

Prince *(Quickly):* Four hundred and nineteen.

Hertford: What was the color of the curtains in the late King's bedchamber?

Prince *(Quickly):* Royal blue, of course.

Hertford: The answers are correct, but they prove nothing.

St. John: Wait! I have a question on which hangs the throne. Where is the Great Seal? Only he who truly was the Prince of Wales can answer that.

Prince *(Confidently):* There is nothing difficult about that. Lord St. John, go to my room in the palace. In the left-hand corner farthest from the door, you will find in the wall a brazen nail head. Press on it and a little jewel case will fly open. No one else in the world knows about that chest. The first thing you will see will be the Great Seal. Bring it here.

Tom: Why do you hesitate? Haven't you heard the King's command? Go!

Prince: Tom, you are indeed loyal to help me this way. I have suffered much these past weeks.

Tom: And I, though I like the comforts of royalty, dearly miss my friends at Offal Court. I have been most concerned about your welfare.

Prince: I have seen much unhappiness and injustice, but when I rule England, I hope what I've seen will help me. I shall give my people the justice they deserve.

TOM: I hope Your Majesty will not mind, but I have already released and pardoned many prisoners.

PRINCE: I do not mind at all, and you shall be rewarded for your generosity and loyalty to me.

NARRATOR: Lord St. John returns carrying the Great Seal.

ST. JOHN: The Great Seal of England!

TOM: Now, my King, take back these regal clothes and give poor Tom, thy servant, his rags again.

LADY: Arrest the impostor!

LORD: To the tower! Hang him.

PRINCE: I will not have this. Were it not for him, I would not have my crown again. Hear my first proclamation as Edward the Sixth: Whereas Tom Canty has been a king, he shall continue to wear royal clothes and all will pay him reverence. He will have the protection of the throne and the support of the crown. He shall be known by the honorable title of the King's Ward.

ALL: Long live the King! Long live the King's Ward! Hurrah!

The End

STORIES FROM THE BIBLE

The Story of Ruth

1. Beyond the River Jordan

It came to pass in days long gone that there was a famine in the land of Israel.

Many Israelites crossed over into the country of Moab, for there was much grain on that side of the river, while in Israel there was none at all.

Among the last to leave was a man named Elimelech, his wife, Naomi, and their two sons. They left the city of Bethlehem in Israel, traveled down into the country of Moab, and made a home for themselves there.

In Moab, the land was rich and pleasant. The sun shone, the wind blew, the rain fell, and the fields were full of grain. The busy, happy years went by. The sons grew to manhood, and each married one of the fair women of Moab.

But when ten years had passed, sorrow came to the household. Elimelech died, and his two sons died. Naomi was left poor and alone with her two daughters-in-law in a strange land.

Naomi said to her daughters-in-law, "I will go back to my own country, to Bethlehem. My kindred dwell there, and I have heard that there is plenty in the land once more. There I can work and fill all my needs."

The two young women said, "We will go with you."

But Naomi replied, "No, stay with your kindred here in your own land. Go, each of you, to your mother's house.

May the Lord be kind to you, as you have been kind to my husband, my sons, and me."

The elder girl kissed Naomi and returned to her own mother. But the younger girl, Ruth, said, "Do not ask me to leave you. For wherever you go, I will go. Wherever you live, there will be my home. Your people will be my people, and your God my God. Where you die, I will also die, and there will I be buried."

Naomi saw that Ruth was steadfast and would not be put off. And so they came to Bethlehem at the beginning of the harvest.

2. THE GLEANER

On every side of the town of Bethlehem, as far as one could see, fields after fields were thick with golden grain. No man could remember a finer crop of barley or wheat. No man could recall a time when the land was so full of plenty.

Before the sun rose above the hills, the reapers began their work. With their hook-shaped sickles they cut the grain handful by handful. After them came young men and boys who had not yet learned to handle the sickle. Some gathered the swaths into bundles. Others tied the bundles into sheaves.

Following these were the gleaners. They were the poor people of the village, and the strangers who did not have homes in the land. They picked up the grain the reapers left behind.

In this land lived a rich and mighty man named Boaz, who was Naomi's kinsman. When Ruth saw the reapers at work

in his fields of waving grain, she said to Naomi, "Let me
follow after the reapers and glean, that we may have food."

"Go, my daughter," said Naomi.

It was near noon when Boaz came down from the city and
stood watching the work of the harvest. He watched the men
and women work their way across the field. Then he asked
one of his servants, "Who is the maiden who follows after the
reapers? She seems to be a stranger to the harvest field."

"It is Ruth, the daughter-in-law of Naomi," the man
replied. "She came back with Naomi out of the country of
Moab. Today she asked to glean among the sheaves. She has
worked from the first light of morning until now."

Then Boaz had Ruth brought before him, and he spoke to her. "Do not go to glean in another field," he said. "Follow my reapers. As you glean, take even of the sheaves, for have I not plenty? When you are thirsty, go to the vessels and drink. When you are hungry, sit down to eat with the maidens of my house, and the men of my house will look after you."

Ruth bowed herself to the ground and thanked Boaz. "But why," she asked, "should you be so kind to a stranger?"

And Boaz answered, "I have been told how you left your father, mother, and the land of your birth, and have come to a strange country to care for your mother-in-law, who is old and alone. May the God of Israel reward you, keep you, and protect you!"

Ruth gleaned in the field until evening. When at last she stood and beat out the grain, it filled a bushel basket almost to the top. Then she took the grain back to the city to give to her mother-in-law, Naomi.

When Naomi heard how Ruth had gleaned in the field of Boaz, and with what kindness he had treated her, her heart was glad within her. "It is good, my daughter," she said. "Go with the maidens of his house each day as he has asked you. Boaz is a good man, and near of kin to us."

So Ruth went into the fields and gleaned of the barley and the wheat until the end of the harvest.

When all of the grain was gathered in and the barns were full, Boaz held a great feast of thanksgiving. The hearts of all were merry, and they feasted until far into the night.

Ruth was there, too. She wore her finest clothes. But no pretty dress or ornament could outshine the goodness in her face.

Boaz said to Ruth, "Because you are as kind as you are beautiful, you shall never know sorrow or want again. You and Naomi will both come into my house, and you I will have for my own dear wife."

So Ruth and Boaz were married, and before long they had a baby boy named Obed. Naomi rocked the baby in her arms and was filled with joy. "God has blessed you," all her friends said.

Naomi knew it was true. She looked down at the sleeping baby and smiled. And they all lived together in great happiness for the rest of their days.

The Story of David

1. The Shepherd Boy

Near the village of Bethlehem there lived an old man who had eight sons. He was so rich, his neighbors called him Jesse, a word that in their language meant "Wealth." His grandfather, whose name was Boaz, had been one of the great men of the land. His grandmother, whose name was Ruth, had been famous for her goodness and beauty.

But while Jesse and his family lived happily in their valley, not far away, the King of Israel was in terrible trouble. He seemed to have lost his senses. He was cruel even to his best friends. There were times when he was so wild that nobody dared go near him.

There was only one thing that seemed to please him, and that was music. So his servants said to him, "Let us seek out for you a skillful player of the harp. He will play when you are troubled, and you shall be well."

The king agreed. One of the servants said, "I have seen a son of Jesse of Bethlehem, a young man who keeps his father's sheep in the valley. No one can play the harp so well as he. Even the beasts like to listen to him."

So the king sent messengers to the little village. They told Jesse that the king wanted to see the lad who tended the sheep, and who played so sweetly on the harp. The old man called the lad from the pastures. The boy's name was David.

He was the youngest of Jesse's eight sons. He was ruddy-faced, slender, and handsome, with eyes as sharp and bright as an eagle's.

Jesse gave his son a donkey loaded with bread, a bottle of wine, and a plump goat and sent him with them to the king.

The king was much pleased with David. The music of the harp cheered his heart until his madness left him, and he was refreshed and well. He took David as a page, and David lived for a whole year in the king's house in his favor.

2. THE GIANT

About this time, a tribe of rude men called the Philistines came up from the south and began to overrun the country. The king sent out his warriors against them, but they were driven back. It looked as though every city and field would fall into the hands of the Philistines. There was only one thing to be done. The king himself must go out at the head of his army, and give battle to his savage foes.

There was no longer any need for the young page in the king's household, for everyone was too busy to listen to music now. So, with his harp on his shoulder, he went back home. He tended his father's sheep as he had before. But his older brothers went out as soldiers in the king's army.

The Philistines pitched their camp on the top of a hill. The Israelites pitched their camp on the top of another hill. There was a broad valley between them. Each army was afraid of the other. Neither wanted to begin the battle. All day and all night they lay there, making great boasts, but doing nothing.

In the morning, a huge giant, who was the champion of the Philistines, went out and stood in the valley midway between the camps. He was called Goliath, and he was more than ten feet tall. He wore a helmet of brass upon his head. He was clad in a coat of armor made of brass and weighing two or three hundred pounds. The shaft of his spear was like a long beam. Its heavy iron point alone was as much as a common man could lift.

Goliath stood in the valley and cried out to the king's army on the mountaintop, "What are you doing up there, you cowards? I defy the armies of Israel this day! I dare the best man among you to come down and fight with me. If he is able to kill me, then we will be your servants. But if I kill him, then you shall be our servants and serve us."

When the king and his warriors heard Goliath's words, they were very much afraid. Not one of them dared make him any answer. For forty days, the two armies lay in camp on the hilltops. Every morning and evening, Goliath went down into the valley and made the same speech.

So it went until food grew scarce. The Israelites would have suffered from hunger if their kinsmen at home had not helped them. And the Philistines would have starved if they had not sent companies out to bring in pillage from the farms.

3. The Army of Israel

One morning, Jesse called David and said, "I hear the king's men have hardly enough to eat. I am afraid that your brothers are hungry. Let one of the hired men take care of the sheep today, and go up to the camp to see how they are getting on. Take a wagon with you, and put corn and bread in it for your brothers. Put in ten cheeses, too, as a present to their captain. Find out how everything is going, then come back and tell me."

David was delighted to be sent on such an errand. He loaded the wagon and set off across the country toward the camp. He had to take a roundabout way, for he was afraid of meeting some of the bands of Philistines who were out foraging.

When he reached the end of his journey, it was late in the afternoon. He found the two armies drawn up in the line of battle, each on its own hilltop. The men on both sides were making a great deal of noise, shouting back and forth and beating their shields. But that was about as near as they ever got to a fight.

David left the wagon with the driver and hurried up the hill to where his brothers were standing. They were glad to see him, and when he told them about the corn and the bread, they thanked him warmly.

While they stood talking on the brow of the hill, Goliath came out into the valley and made his speech. All the men who were near ran back to their tents in fear.

But when David saw and heard him, he said, "Who is this man that he should defy the army of Israel? And what shall be done for the man who kills this Philistine?"

"The king has offered to give him a chest full of gold and one of his daughters for his wife. And he will make his father and brothers rulers among the people."

"I don't see how the king can offer more," said the lad. "I will try my hand against the giant myself."

His older brothers laughed at him. "You proud little upstart," they said, "go home and tend your sheep."

But David went to the king and said, "Israel's heart should not fail because of a man. I will go and fight this Philistine."

The king replied, "David, you play sweet music, but you cannot fight the Philistine. Why, you are only a boy, and he is a man of war, trained to fight from his youth!"

David stood tall and said, "I used to keep my father's sheep. When a lion or a bear came and took a lamb out of the flock, I went after it, struck it with my staff, and delivered the lamb from its mouth. When the beast turned and came after me, I caught it by its beard, struck it, and killed it. I have killed both the lion and the bear. This giant will be like one of them, seeing as how he has defied the armies of Israel."

He continued, "God delivered me from the paw of the lion and the paw of the bear. He will deliver me from the hand of this Philistine."

Said the king, "Go, then, and may God be with you!"

4. THE SLING

The king clothed David in his own armor, and set a helmet of bronze upon his head. David fastened the sword to his armor and tried to walk. But he could barely move, for he had never worn armor before.

And David said to the king, "I cannot walk with these. I have never practiced in armor." So David took them off.

With nothing in his hands but his shepherd's staff and a sling, he went out in the morning to meet the giant. On his way down the hill, he crossed a brook. There he chose for himself five smooth stones, and put them in the pouch he carried by his side.

By this time, Goliath had come out into the valley. He was making the speech that he had made so often before, daring the Israelites to send out a man to fight him. When he saw the boy coming down the hill with only a shepherd's staff in his hand, he laughed.

"Do you think I am a dog," he roared, "that you send a boy out against me with a stick? Come on, my little fellow, and I will feed your flesh to the birds and the beasts!"

Then David said to Goliath, "You come to me with a sword and a spear. But I come to you in the name of the God of the army of Israel, whom you have defied. This day, the Lord will deliver you into my hand."

Then Goliath was very angry. He strode forward across the valley, shaking his great spear. But David was not at all afraid of him. He ran down the hill to meet him. As he ran, he took one of the smooth stones he had picked up, and put it into his sling.

Goliath raised his spear to throw it, but David was much quicker. He twirled the sling once, twice, three times—and the stone went whizzing through the air and struck Goliath in the forehead. It struck so hard that it sunk deep into the giant's head, and he fell upon his face to the ground. David ran and stood upon him, drew Goliath's big sword from its sheath, and cut off the giant's head. And that was the end of Goliath.

When the Philistines saw that their champion was dead, they fled down the far side of the hill. The Israelites shouted and ran after them, and did not stop until they had chased them out of the country.

Everyone praised David for what he had done. The king took him into his own house and made him captain of a thousand men. As they marched through the land, the women and girls came out from the cities, singing and playing tambourines.

David was no longer looked upon as a boy, but as a prince. After a time, he married the king's daughter. And when the king and his son were both slain in battle, the Israelites chose David to be their ruler.

Daniel in the Lion's Den

1

Far from Israel, in the empire of Persia, there lived an old man of such courage and wisdom that he cared only to do right, no matter what the cost. He was called Daniel which, in the language of that time, meant "God is my judge."

Many years before, the Persians had conquered Israel and taken its people prisoner. Daniel was one of the prisoners of the Persians. But even so, the king of the Persians gave Daniel a place of high honor and great power. He made Daniel first among the princes and governors of the land, for he saw that Daniel was wise and able to rule.

This made the other princes and rulers very jealous. They tried to find some evil in Daniel, so that they could speak against him to the king. But they could find no fault in him or his ways.

Then they saw that three times each day, Daniel went to his room and opened the window that faced the city of Jerusalem. Looking toward Jerusalem, Daniel made his prayer to God. Jerusalem was in ruins, and the Temple was no longer standing. But Daniel prayed three times each day with his face toward the place where the house of God had once stood, though it was many hundreds of miles away.

The jealous princes thought that in Daniel's prayers they could find a way to do him harm, or perhaps even have him put to death. So they went to the king and said, "We have agreed to make a law that for thirty days, no one shall ask anything of any god or man save you, O king. And if anyone shall pray to any god, or ask anything from any man save you during the thirty days, he shall be thrown into the den where the lions are kept."

The king was not a wise man. He was foolish and vain. He was pleased with this law that would set him even above the gods.

"Now, O king," said the flattering princes, "sign this writing and make the law, so that it cannot be changed. For no law among the Persians can be altered."

So, without asking Daniel's advice, the king signed the writing. The law was made, and the word was sent out through the kingdom: for thirty days, no one might pray to any god or ask a favor of any man save the king. The price of disobedience was death.

2

When Daniel found out that the law had been made, he went home. And in his upper room, with his windows open toward Jerusalem, he knelt down and prayed. He prayed three times that day, giving thanks to God, just as he had done before.

Nearby, the men were watching. They saw Daniel kneeling in prayer to God. Then they went to the king and said, "O king, did you not make a law that if anyone in thirty days offers a prayer to any god, he shall be cast into the den of lions?"

"It is true," replied the king. "The law has been made. It cannot be altered."

The men said, "There is one man who does not obey your law. It is Daniel, one of the prisoners from Israel. He prays to

his God three times every day, just as he did before you signed the law."

The king was greatly displeased with his foolishness, for he saw how he had been tricked. He loved Daniel, and knew that no one in the kingdom could take his place. All day, until the sun went down, he tried to find some way to save Daniel's life. But when evening came, the men returned, and told him that the law must be kept.

Very unwillingly, the king sent for Daniel and gave the order that he should be thrown into the den of lions. But the king spoke to Daniel, saying, "Your God will deliver you."

And so Daniel was taken and cast into the den of lions. A heavy stone was rolled over the mouth of the den. Then the king and the princes sealed it, each with his personal mark, so that no one would take away the stone and let Daniel out.

Then the king went away to his palace. But he would neither eat nor listen to his musicians. All night, he did not sleep a wink, because he was worrying and wondering about Daniel.

Very early in the morning, the king rose from his bed and went in haste to the den of lions. He pushed away the stone. In a voice full of sorrow he called out, scarcely hoping to hear an answer, "O Daniel, has your God been able to deliver you from the lions?"

And out of the darkness came Daniel's strong voice, saying, "O king, may you live forever! My God sent his angel and shut the lions' mouths. They have not hurt me, because my God saw that I had done no wrong. O king, I have done no wrong before you."

The king was extremely glad. He gave his servants orders to take Daniel out of the lion's den. Daniel was brought out safe and without harm.

And Daniel stood beside the king until the end of his reign, and also afterward while the next king ruled over the lands of Persia.

POETRY

SEASONAL CHANGE

JUNE
by Aileen Fisher

The day is warm
and a breeze is blowing,
the sky is blue
and its eye is glowing,
and everything's new
and green and growing …

My shoes are off
and my socks are showing …

My socks are off …

Do you know how I'm going?

BAREFOOT!

SUMMER RAIN
by Elizabeth Coatsworth

What could be lovelier than to hear
    the summer rain
    cutting across the heat as scythes
    cut across grain?
    Falling upon the steaming roof
    with sweet uproar,
    tapping and rapping wildly
    at the door?

No, do not lift the latch,
    but through the pane
    we'll stand and watch the circus pageant
    of the rain,
    and see the lightning, like a tiger,
    striped and dread,
    and hear the thunder cross the shaken sky
    with elephant tread.

SUMMER RAIN

by Eve Merriam

A shower, a sprinkle,
A tangle, a tinkle,
Greensilver runs the rain.

Like salt on your nose,
Like stars on your toes,
Tingles the tangy rain.

A tickle, a trickle,
A million-dot freckle
Speckles the spotted rain.

Like a cinnamon
Geranium
Smells the rainingest rain!

THAT WAS SUMMER

by Marci Ridlon

Have you ever smelled summer?
Sure you have.
Remember that time
when you were tired of running
or doing nothing much
and you were hot
and you flopped right down on the ground?
Remember how the warm soil smelled
and the grass?
That was summer.

Remember that time
when the storm blew up quick
and you stood under a ledge
and watched the rain till it stopped
and when it stopped
you walked out again to the sidewalk,
the quiet sidewalk?
Remember how the pavement smelled—
all steamy warm and wet?
That was summer.

Remember that time
when you were trying to climb
higher in the tree
and you didn't know how
and your foot was hurting in the fork
but you were holding tight
to the branch?
Remember how the bark smelled then –
all dusty dry, but nice?
That was summer.

If you try very hard
can you remember that time
when you played outside all day
and you came home for dinner
and had to take a bath right away,
right away?
It took you a long time to pull
your shirt over your head.
Do you remember smelling the sunshine?
That was summer.

THE CITY OF FALLING LEAVES

by Amy Lowell

Leaves fall,
Brown leaves,
Yellow leaves streaked with brown.
They fall,
Flutter,
Fall again.
The brown leaves,
And the streaked yellow leaves,
Loosen on their branches
And drift slowly downwards.
One,
One, two, three,
One, two, five.
All Venice is a falling of Autumn leaves—
Brown,
And yellow streaked with brown.

THE LEAVES DO NOT MIND AT ALL

by Annette Wynne

The leaves do not mind at all
That they must fall.
When summertime has gone,
It is pleasant to put on
A traveling coat of brown and gray
And fly away,
Past the barn and past the school,
Past the noisy little pool
It used to hear but could not see.
Oh, it is joy to be
A leaf—and free!
To be swiftly on the wing
Like a bird adventuring.
And then, tired out, to creep
Under some friendly rail and go to sleep;
The leaves do not mind at all
That they must fall.

AUTUMN WOODS

by James S. Tippett

I like the woods
     In autumn
When dry leaves hide the ground,
When the trees are bare
And the wind sweeps by
With a lonesome rushing sound.

I can rustle the leaves
     In autumn
And I can make a bed
In the thick dry leaves
That have fallen
From the bare trees
Overhead.

FALL

by Aileen L. Fisher

The last of October
We lock the garden gate.
(The flowers have all withered
That used to stand straight.)

The last of October
We put the swings away
And the porch looks deserted
Where we liked to play.

The last of October
The birds have all flown,
The screens are in the attic,
The sandpile's alone:

Everything is put away
Before it starts to snow—
I wonder if the ladybugs
Have any place to go!

WINTER, THE HUNTSMAN
by Osbert Sitwell

Through his iron glades
Rides Winter the Huntsman.
All colour fades
As his horn is heard sighing.

Far through the forest
His wild hooves crash and thunder
Till many a mighty branch
Is torn asunder.

As the red reynard creeps
To his hole near the river,
The copper leaves fall
And the bare trees shiver.

As night creeps from the ground,
Hides each tree from its brother,
And each dying sound
Reveals yet another.

Is it Winter the Huntsman
Who gallops through his iron glades,
Cracking his cruel whip
To the gathering shades?

FALLING SNOW
Anonymous

See the pretty snowflakes
   Falling from the sky;
On the walk and housetop
   Soft and thick they lie.

On the window-ledges
   On the branches bare;
Now how fast they gather,
   Filling all the air.

Look into the garden,
   Where the grass was green;
Covered by the snowflakes,
Not a blade is seen.

Now the bare black bushes
   All look soft and white,
Every twig is laden—
   What a pretty sight!

ON A SNOWY DAY
by Dorothy Aldis

Fence posts wear marshmallow hats
On a winter's day,

Bushes in their nightgowns
Are kneeling down to pray,

And trees spread out their snowy skirts
Before they dance away.

SNOWFLAKES
by Marchette Chute

I once thought that snowflakes were feathers
   And that they came falling down
When the Moon Lady feathered her chickens
   And shook out her silver gown.

And then I began to look closer,
   And now I know just what they are—
I caught one today in my mitten,
   And there was a baby star.

APRIL

by Sara Teasdale

The roofs are shining from the rain,
    The sparrows twitter as they fly,
And with a windy April grace
    The little clouds go by.

Yet the back-yards are bare and brown
    With only one unchanging tree—
I could not be so sure of Spring
    Save that it sings in me.

APRIL

by Eunice Tietjens

The tulips now are pushing up
Like small green knuckles through the ground.
The grass is young and doubtful yet.
The robin takes a look around.
And if you listen you can hear
Spring laughing with a windy sound.

In Time of Silver Rain
by Langston Hughes

In time of silver rain
The earth
Puts forth new life again,
Green grasses grow
And flowers lift their heads,
And over all the plain
The wonder spreads
    Of life,
    Of life,
    Of life!

In time of silver rain
The butterflies
Lift silken wings
To catch a rainbow cry,
And trees put forth
New leaves to sing
In joy beneath the sky
As down the roadway
Passing boys and girls
Go singing, too,
In time of silver rain
    When spring
    And life
    Are new.

SPRING

by Karla Kuskin

I'm shouting
I'm singing
I'm swinging through trees
I'm winging skyhigh
With the buzzing black bees.
I'm the sun
I'm the moon
I'm the dew on the rose.
I'm a rabbit
Whose habit
Is twitching his nose.
I'm lively
I'm lovely
I'm kicking my heels.
I'm crying "Come dance"
To the fresh water eels.
I'm racing through meadows
Without any coat
I'm a gamboling lamb
I'm a light leaping goat
I'm a bud
I'm a bloom
I'm a dove on the wing.
I'm running on rooftops
And welcoming spring!

POETRY

PASSING MOMENTS

THE ARROW AND THE SONG
by Henry Wadsworth Longfellow

I shot an arrow into the air,
It fell to earth, I knew not where;
For, so swiftly it flew, the sight
Could not follow it in its flight.

I breathed a song into the air,
It fell to earth, I knew not where;
For who has sight so keen and strong
That it can follow the flight of song?

Long, long afterward, in an oak
I found the arrow, still unbroke;
And the song, from beginning to end,
I found again in the heart of a friend.

This Is Just to Say
by William Carlos Williams

I have eaten
the plums
that were in
the icebox

and which
you were probably
saving
for breakfast

Forgive me
they were delicious
so sweet
and so cold

The White Horse
by D. H. Lawrence

The youth walks up to the white horse, to put its halter on
And the horse looks at him in silence.
They are so silent they are in another world.

THE SIDEWALK RACER
or On a Skateboard
by Lillian Morrison

Skimming
an asphalt sea
I swerve, I curve, I
sway; I speed to whirring
sound an inch above the
ground; I'm the sailor
and the sail, I'm the
driver and the wheel
I'm the one and only
single engine
human auto
mobile.

CHILD ON TOP OF A GREENHOUSE
by Theodore Roethke

The wind billowing out the seat of my britches,
My feet crackling splinters of glass and dried putty,
The half-grown chrysanthemums staring up like accusers,
Up through the streaked glass, flashing with sunlight,
A few white clouds all rushing eastward,
A line of elms plunging and tossing like horses,
And everyone, everyone pointing up and shouting!

THE BASE STEALER
by Robert Francis

Poised between going on and back, pulled
Both ways taut like a tightrope-walker,
Fingertips pointing the opposites,
Now bouncing tiptoe like a dropped ball
Or a kid skipping rope, come on, come on,
Running a scattering of steps sidewise,
How he teeters, skitters, tingles, teases,
Taunts them, hovers like an ecstatic bird,
He's only flirting, crowd him, crowd him,
Delicate, delicate, delicate, delicate—now!

SONG FORM
by Imamu Amiri Baraka

Morning uptown, quiet on the street,
no matter the distinctions that can be
made, quiet, very quiet, on the street.
Sun's not even up, just some kid and me,
skating, both of us, at the early sun, and
amazed there is grace for us, without our
having to smile too tough, or be very pleasant
even to each other. Merely to be mere, ly to be

THE RIVER IS A PIECE OF SKY

by John Ciardi

From the top of a bridge
The river below
Is a piece of sky—
    Until you throw
    A penny in
    Or a cockleshell
    Or a pebble or two
    Or a bicycle bell
    Or a cobblestone
    Or a fat man's cane—
And then you can see
It's a river again.

The difference you'll see
When you drop your penny:
The river has splashes,
The sky hasn't any.

THE TIDE IN THE RIVER

by Eleanor Farjeon

The tide in the river,
The tide in the river,
The tide in the river runs deep.
I saw a shiver
Pass over the river
As the tide turned in its sleep.

SNOW TOWARD EVENING

by Melville Cane

Suddenly the sky turned gray,
The day,
Which had been bitter and chill,
Grew intensely soft and still.
Quietly
From some invisible blossoming tree
Millions of petals cool and white
Drifted and blew,
Lifted and flew,
Fell with the falling night.

February Twilight
by Sara Teasdale

I stood beside a hill
    Smooth with new-laid snow,
A single star looked out
    From the cold evening glow.

There was no other creature
    That saw what I could see—
I stood and watched the evening star
    As long as it watched me.

The Eagle
by Alfred Tennyson

He clasps the crag with crooked hands;
Close to the sun in lonely lands,
Ring'd with the azure world, he stands.

The wrinkled sea beneath him crawls;
He watches from his mountain walls,
And like a thunderbolt he falls.

A Bird Came Down the Walk

by Emily Dickinson

A Bird came down the Walk—
He did not know I saw—
He bit an Angleworm in halves
And ate the fellow, raw,

And then he drank a Dew
From a convenient Grass—
And then hopped sideways to the Wall
To let a Beetle pass—

He glanced with rapid eyes
That hurried all around—
They looked like frightened Beads, I thought—
He stirred his Velvet Head

Like one in danger, Cautious,
I offered him a Crumb
And he unrolled his feathers
And rowed him softer home—

Than Oars divide the Ocean,
Too silver for a seam—
Or Butterflies, off Banks of Noon
Leap, plashless as they swim.

TEXT CREDITS AND SOURCES

Stories

"Ali and the Magic Stew" Reprinted by permission of *Cricket* magazine, November 2000, Vol. 28, No. 3, © 2000 by Shulamith Levey Oppenheim

"Fire on the Mountain" from *The Fire on the Mountain and other Stories from Ethopia and Eritrea* by Harold Courlander and Wolf Leslau. Copyright 1978 by Harold Courlander and Wolf Leslau. Reprinted by permission of The Emma Courlander Trust.

"The Prince and the Pauper" (play) is reprinted with permission of *Plays* Magazine, copyright 1995, Kalmbach Publishing Co., 21027 Crossroads Circle, Waukesha, WI 53187-1612. Web: www.playsmag.com

"Salt and Bread" from *Ride With the Sun*, edited by Harold Courlander, copyright © 1983 by Harold Courlander. Reprinted by permission of the Emma Courlander Trust.

Poems

"Autumn Woods" by James S. Tippett, copyright © 1933, copyright renewed © 1973 by Martha K. Tippett

"The Base Stealer" by Robert Francis from *The Orb Weaver* © 1960 by Robert Francis. Reprinted by permission of the Wesleyan University Press.

"Child on Top of a Greenhouse" by Theodore Roethke, copyright 1946 by Editorial Publications, Inc. From *The Collected Poems of Theodore Roethke* by Theodore Roethke. Used by permission of Doubleday, a division of Random House, Inc.

"Fall" by Aileen Fisher from *Always Wondering* by Aileen Fisher, copyright © 1991 by Aileen Fisher. Used by permission of Marian Reiner for the author.

"In Time of Silver Rain" from *The Collected Poems of Langston Hughes* by Langston Hughes, copyright © 1994 by The Estate of Langston Hughes. Used by permission of Alfred A. Knopf, a division of Random House, Inc.

"June" by Aileen Fisher from *Going Barefoot* by Aileen Fisher, copyright © 1960, 1988 by Aileen Fisher. Used by permission of Marian Reiner for the author.

"On a Snowy Day" from *All Together* by Dorothy Aldis, copyright 1925-1928, 1934, 1939, 1952, renewed 1953, © 1954-1956, 1962 by Dorothy Aldis, © by Roy E. Porter, renewed. Used by permission of G.P. Putnam's Sons, an imprint of Penguin Putnam Books for Young Readers, a division of Penguin Putnam, Inc.

"The Sidewalk Racer" by Lillian Morrison from *Way To Go! Sports Poems* by Lillian Morrison, Wordsong/Boyds Mills Press, copyright © 2001 by Lillian Morrison. Used by permission of Marian Reiner for the author.

"Snowflakes" by Marcette Chute from *Around and About* by Marcette Chute, © 1957 by E. P. Dutton. Copyright renewed 1985 by Marcette Chute. Reprinted by permission of Elizabeth Hauser.

"Song Form" by LeRoi Jones (Imamu Amiri Baraka). Reprinted by permission of Sterling Lord Literistic, Inc. Copyright Amiri Baraka. [Copyright date unavailable.]

"Summer Rain" by Eve Merriam from *There Is No Rhyme for Silver* by Eve Merriam, copyright © 1962, 1990 by Eve Merriam. Used by permission of Marian Reiner.

"This Is Just to Say" by William Carlos Williams from *Collected Poems: 1909-1939, Volume I*, copyright 1938 by New Directions Publishing Corp. Reprinted by permission of New Directions Publishing Corp.

"The White Horse" by D. H. Lawrence from *The Complete Poems of D.H. Lawrence* by D. H. Lawrence, edited by V. de Sola Pinto & F. W. Roberts, copyright © 1964, 1971 by Angelo Ravagli and C. M. Weekly, Executors of the Estate of Frieda Lawrence Ravagli. Used by permission of Viking Penguin, a division of Penguin Putnam Inc.

"Winter the Huntsman" by Osbert Sitwell from *Selected Poems Old and New*, Gerald Duckworth and Company Ltd., 1943. Reprinted by permission of David Higham and Associates.

Other selections adapted from:

Beautiful Bible Stories for Children, by Rev. Jesse Lyman Hurlbut (Philadelphia: The John C. Winston Company, 1902)

Children's Stories and How to Tell Them, by J. Berg Esenwein and Marietta Stockard (Springfield, Mass.: The Home Correspondence School, 1917)

Fifty Famous Stories Retold, by James Baldwin (New York: American Book Company, 1896)

Old Stories of the East, by James Baldwin (New York: American Book Company, 1895)

Old Peter's Russian Tales, by Arthur Ransome (London: Jonathan Cape Ltd., 1916)

School Reading by Grades, Fifth Year, by James Baldwin (New York: American Book Company, 1897)

While every care has been taken to trace and acknowledge copyright, the editors tender their apologies for any accidental infringement when copyright has proven untraceable. They would be pleased to include the appropriate acknowledgement in any subsequent edition of this publication.

Editor: John Holdren

Art Director: Steve Godwin

Designer: Jayoung Cho

Illustrators:
Jayoung Cho
Deborah Wolfe Ltd. (Rob Kemp, Jeff LeVan, Richard Waldrep)

Copyright © 2002, 2003 K12 Inc. All rights reserved.

No part of this document may be reproduced or used in any form or by any means, graphic, electronic, or mechanical, including photocopying, recording, taping, and information retrieval systems, without the prior written permission of K12 Inc.

ISBN: 1-931728-38-0

Printed by Worzalla, Stevens Point, WI, USA, April 2015, Lot 042015